Girl-Shaped Shadows

by
Miles Truckenbrod

A Division of Windy City Publishers

Chicago, IL

Girl-Shaped Shadows

Copyright © 2011 by Miles Truckenbrod

Second City Books
2118 Plum Grove Rd., #349
Rolling Meadows, IL 60008
www.secondcitybooks.com

Published in the United States of America

First Edition: July 2011

ISBN: 978-1-935766-02-5

Library of Congress Control Number: 2011932263

It is only fitting this novella not be dedicated to anyone,
because it was not written with any dedication.

The only dedication necessary will be
what it takes to finish it.

—The Voice of Reason

"It all comes down to nothing."

Dave Matthews Band
Typical Situation

The First Chapter

Eleven Sentences

A few short minutes after crossing into the northwest corner of Arkansas on Interstate 540, or Highway 71 as it was once known, I could see the Embassy Suites hotel standing proudly in the distance. The rooftop glass pyramid pointing toward the clouds.

I was back.

A mild grin came across my face as I gazed at the building, remembering my stay there only two years prior, and how my current visit was for a completely different reason, a whole other purpose. My mind quickly began to race as a nervous energy rattled my gut. I was overwhelmed by a million and one thoughts on how this could go wrong. And only one thought on how it could go right. This was the building where it could all go down. I'll either sleep alone tonight, or I won't.

It was that simple.

It was approaching 12:30 on a Saturday afternoon, in February of 2006.

The Second Chapter

Requisite

I once sat, on the first day of class, in a college course on the History of Western Civilization. I'm sorry, I'm sorry. Let me correct myself. I once sat, on the first day of class, in a *community* college course on the History of Western Civilization. Wanted to make sure I was clear on that. The professor began his lecture by asking the class, "How does history come to be? How does it begin?"

How does history begin?

Obviously not a single one of us unmotivated students attempted to answer the professor's question or make even the slightest attempt to raise one of our hands. So after a few moments of silence and a couple of 180 degree classroom scans from the professor waiting for an answer, his grin faded, and his mouth opened. "Okay. Well I'll tell you. One word ... and it's a big one! Are you ready? Cause here it comes ... this is exciting, isn't it?" He stuck his arms out as if preaching to a congregation. "Writing," the clearly over-enthused history professor bellowed out. "Writing. It all begins with, and comes down to, writing."

All that build-up and all the man says is writing?

"Hey ... hey," some dude sitting behind me said under his breath as he hit my shoulder. "I thought he was gonna say, like, sex or somethin'. You know ... all things on earth doin' it with each other. That's where life comes from. You know, man?"

"Uhhhhh..., " was the only verbal response I could give this fellow while still maintaining a straight face. We weren't even talking about life, we were talking about history. Actually my response wasn't even verbal, it was just some random sound. But the moron did get me thinking. Thinking, "GOD AM I BORED AS SHIT! What kind of a life is this?" I mean, I was an unmotivated nineteen year old sitting in a community college classroom, which in itself screams *NO DIRECTION!* listening to a stocky history teacher ramble on about his thoughts on the beginning of the past, meanwhile sitting in front of some ingrate who genuinely believed history came to be as a result of everything simply banging everything else.

But alas, I was no better than anyone else in that classroom. It was merely another pre-requisite course someone told me I had to take, along with a bunch of other 'pre' courses that were supposed to lead up to some sort of requisite. Well, requisite was not being found at the community college, or at my twelve-hour shift factory job, or at some random house party I was dragged to where I just stood by some stranger's electric range with a handle of Southern Comfort in one hand and a shot glass in the other, occasionally chasing with some Dr. Pepper, staring at everyone else wondering why or how I still hadn't gotten laid by this point in my life, all the while fully realizing that no chick at this party had low enough self-respect to change that.

I simply wasn't that guy.

Nope. The only requisite I had found was a homely stripper by that same name. What sort of a stage name is that anyway? She just happened to work at a joint that didn't serve booze, so your average late-teen drifter could just walk in and take in a show. Every time I walked through the door of that place it felt as if I was walking into a tool shed or someone's old, dark garage. Except you didn't see any antique lawn mowers or hedge trimmers lying around. What you saw were antique men sitting at a dry bar gazing at the stage, perhaps wondering how their life had taken them to that point, or if lap dances were negotiable. Yet judging by the scar tissue parade that was up on stage, I'm sure a few of the guys there, old and young, were wishing the place was an old garage so they could have access to a nice, hot car tailpipe for which they could wrap their lips around.

You walk in to these higher end strip joints where the talent is a bit classier and you know what most of those dancers are on stage thinking? They're thinking, "Damn am I good at what I do. I'm going to take home my thousand bucks tonight and pay rent tomorrow for my amazing apartment in the city. Then I think I'll take my boyfriend shopping and out to eat, but tuition is due in a couple of weeks so I shouldn't spend too much. That guy at the end of the stage is wearing an expensive suit ... jackpot!" On the contrary, the "help" at these middle of nowhere, low-end joints I was frequenting are on stage thinking, "Someone please end me. I wish the landlord would stop calling me about my backed rent! I need baby formula and diapers. I think I'm pregnant again. Who could the father be? This dude at the end of the stage is wearing a cutoff and has a pony tail … won't make rent again this month. Maybe if I offer to take him home for the night he'll pay my electric bill up to date."

But let's get serious. How much difference is there between the average low-class strip joint and your standard 4-H cattle show? Think abou tit. Oops. Ha! I meant to type "think about it" but hit the space bar a letter too early. I'm just gonna leave that tiny Freudian slip in there for good measure. Anyway, strippers vs. cattle. Both walk out onto some platform, they move around a small area, people stare at them and make judgments, they get money (prizes) presented to them, occasionally they're smacked in the rear, and then walk off into the darkness just so another bovine can be sent out. I suppose the same could be said about higher class strip clubs as well, but they lack one key aspect low end joints share with cattle shows. Lactation. The similarities are overwhelming, don't you think?

But then Requisite would slowly walk onto the stage, and my harsh judgments of these women would dissipate. Quite unfair of me to view them with such haste while I was throwing singles up on stage. I enjoyed Requisite though, because she never did herself up too much. She had this naturalness to her that was, I don't know, refreshing I guess. I mean, she wasn't noticeably gorgeous or anything, but I know I realized a classiness within her which I was positive most of the other patrons overlooked. She always displayed a confidence, even while men were hoarding dollar bills into her g-string. It was almost as if she knew she should be making a living doing something else, but chose to give her best at what she was doing. I admired that about her. Perhaps I should have mentioned that to her once. But I never did.

I think to myself now that Requisite, a stripper, is someone's friend … sister … daughter. Possibly the daughter of that chubby community college history professor I once had. That professor, whom despite his over-confidence and overall general lack of appeal, was correct. It does all start with writing. So that's what I'm going to do. Write. Write with the same confidence and attitude as the professor's could-be pole dancing daughter. I *need* to tell my story. What is *requisite* but another word for *necessary*? And without writing, how else could my story be told? How else could it become part of history?

The Third Chapter

The Voice of Reason

"Strippers vs. cattle? Seriously? That is how you choose to begin this little, uh, whatever it is you're doing here, Miles? I mean, honestly, your family members, at best, are probably the only people that are going to read this thing. Should you not focus more on them being your target audience, and perhaps not start out by comparing under-achieving exotic dancers with farm animals?"

"Okay, see, this is what I've never understood. Why try focusing and aiming everything one writes to a certain audience? Is it such a literary travesty to simply write, and then proceed to just let the piece be, and let it speak for itself? Let people take what they will from it? My family has a great sense of humor by the way, I know they'll enjoy it."

"I'm sure they would enjoy it if it was actually *funny*! But you're right. It is every family's dream to read about their loved ones going out and motorboating every stripper in the tri-county area. Let me tell you a little something about stripper dust. You get high off of it for the following reason. It contains a special intoxicant that senses lonely, depressed men. Once that spore finds a host subject, such as your pathetic self, it latches on and induces a euphoric state, leading that depressed subject to believe its worries are gone, and it's appealable to women, when in fact the subject is not. This euphoric state lasts until the subject leaves the premise of the stripping establishment and meanders back to its demeaning residency, a flaccid studio apartment in your case, where upon arrival, the spores dissipate, leaving the subject in a state of complete and udder failure. It is then when the subject realizes the only way to be jovial in life is to attend the aforementioned establishment and repeat the process all over. It's science."

"Oh, God help us! My sin of motorboating! The world is coming to an end. Brace yourselves! I refuse to be labeled as a subject regarding the 'science' of stripping. An entire collection of books could be written about the far worse things that are done in this world."

"You're right, Miles. The first book in that collection could be about your meaningless attempt at actually writing one. That's terrifying! Luckily you're in the unique position you are, in that your time is so worthless and invaluable, only your own personal time is being wasted, because no one else is going to waste their precious time reading this monstrosity. And what the hell was with that first chapter? Shortest and most pointless opening chapter of any novel in history I'm presuming, but I may check with your old stocky history professor on that one. I mean, way to grab the reader's attention and then reel 'em in! Embassy Suites and Northwest Arkansas? Fascinating."

"Love your support. Do you really think I'm just going to briefly mention Northwest Arkansas and leave it at that? A person cannot just talk about NW Arkansas in passing and then not go back to it. And I'm just going to say this here at the beginning. This is definitely, for lack of a better term, an R-rated book. But what's the point of writing anything if stuff is just going to be held back? All I ask of the readers is that they come into this book with an open mind. And what business of yours is any of this anyway? I can't believe you're being *this* negative only three chapters in!"

"Miles, let's use the term 'chapters' loosely, alright? What you have here so far are poorly worded sentences, several incomplete mind you, which are riddled with grammatical errors. The first 'chapter' is merely eleven sentences long. Eleven. Which, by the way, you idiotically point out ... IN THE CHAPTER'S TITLE!! A more unoriginal idea I cannot recall. Your first chapter really should be the prologue, but I know you're trying to milk as many chapters as you can out of this so you can tell people it's a high number. Is this novel going to consistently continue in this manner? 'Novel': also used loosely."

"It's a bit unfair to so hastily judge based solely on what is here so far, don't you think? Granted, it's not much, but it's a start, which is the largest hurdle to overcome. Once something is actually started, then hopefully it will hit the ground running."

"Oh, Miles, this'll hit the ground alright, it just won't go anywhere. I mean, who reads books anymore anyway that aren't about wizards, or vampires, or conspiracy theories? All subjects of which I highly doubt you have the writing capability to pull off. You haven't even described yourself for God's sake, or told anyone who the hell I am or why I'm here. Am I even going to get a name, or are you just going to argue with a nameless person for the duration of this thing? Readers want to know this sort of stuff! Maybe you could call me Niles. Am I simply your other persona? The other half of your split personality? You're just like Gollum from *The Lord of the Rings* trilogy, except not as funny and less attractive. Actually, there you go. You should write three of these failures as a series and call it *The Douchebag Trilogy*."

"I'm sure some people do want to know those kinds of things, but it goes along the same line as not writing or focusing to just one particular audience. People can picture me as however their imaginations allow. That's the beauty of books. You on the other hand? It's complicated. You're here for a number of different reasons that I'd rather not bore the reader with. I'll just say that for whatever reason I feel a strong necessity to have you around. But keep in mind that I'll write you out of this thing without batting an eye. Your negativity regarding this venture is already wearing thin on me. Hell, you already stole the opportunity for me to dedicate this book to anyone!"

"Well that was a garbage explanation. I'm sure literary agents you send this to will just jump at the opportunity to represent a writer that can't explain his own work, refuses to acknowledge a particular audience, and invents a character merely for the purpose of arguing with. And believe you me, I did a favor to whomever you were going to dedicate this book to. But yes, I do agree the reader should feel free to use their imagination. Yet maybe a lot of people don't want to constantly do that, and how can people use their imagination with zero description? It's your responsibility as the writer to describe things for them. Your laziness is becoming rapidly apparent. And you don't have the balls to write me out. I am a highly more fascinating character which I'm confident the reader will look forward to hearing from. They'll probably skip over pages just to read what I have to say! Plus, you should be thankful you have me here anyway. I mean, are you so self-absorbed and unoriginal that you have to make *yourself* a character in your first book? Who does that? Obviously you have genuine confidence problems. But you go ahead with your little project here, Miles. I'll even try not to chime in too often. I'm sure this will end up being quite the literary achievement. Probably rank right up there with *Sisterhood of the Traveling Pants*."

"Actually, I think the opposite will prove true. I believe readers are going to be quite put off by you and your bull-shit. And for your information, *Sisterhood of the Traveling Pants* was a best-seller, and spun off some movies."

"Oh yeah? Well I'm sure your piece of writing here will also end up being a big seller! Probably end up on the same best-seller list as a pamphlet on how to avoid Gonorrhea."

The Fourth Chapter

A Mild Obsession

To become a greeter at Wal-Mart, one need only meet or exceed a single requirement: he or she must be at least ninety-five years old. Ninety-four just isn't going to cut it! The cutoff age for this position, of course, is death. Rigor mortis. Wal-Mart does not want their customers greeted by a decaying human corpse or skeletal structure with pull strings attached to their jaw which moves every time someone enters the sliding doors. *Welcome to Wal-Mart.* I do not think it's simply an easy walk-on job either. I believe that wannabe greeters have to fulfill a rigorous two-week training course on how to properly use the price gun that is needed for returns. God-forbid someone takes an already purchased item to customer service without a bright pink sticker attached. You've got to give it up for the greeters however. Rarely do I enter a Wal-Mart and not have a cart waiting for me, despite the fact that more often than not the cart has at least one dysfunctional wheel.

I only mention this to segue into three simple words: I. LOVE. WAL-MART. Now I am well aware those three words may be the stopping point for a few of the dozen or so people who actually read this book, as there are many a folk out there who do not share my enthusiasm for the world's largest company. I understand. I'll get to that. Just please allow me a moment or two to explain myself.

My familiarity with Wal-Mart was hoist upon me at a very early age. I have fond memories from childhood about taking trips to Wal-Mart with my mother. The nearest location was a solid fifteen minute drive from my hometown, so you can imagine my excitement whenever my mom would tell me we were going to Wal-Mart. It wasn't just for the fact I knew I would be taking a ride in the car, it also meant I would get to spend some quality time with mom, which was, and still is, just so wonderful.

I distinctly remember one time, and I was very young, leaving Wal-Mart with mom and heading to the car. I got into the back seat and started to feel really uneasy for some reason or another. I felt as if I was going to lose it at any given time. Since mothers have a sixth sense about these sorts of things, she started to unbuckle my seatbelt in hopes of getting me out of the car before I got sick. However, despite her best efforts, and the lack of control I have since built, I threw up all down the front of myself in the back seat of our Chevy Nova. I immediately started to cry, but mom didn't skip a beat. She got that soiled shirt off of me right away and put it in an empty Wal-Mart bag (just one of their many uses). She cleaned me up, and then as if she had known something was going to happen, she pulled out a package of Fruit of the Loom white tees she had bought for me not five minutes prior. She whipped one of those shirts on me, made sure I was feeling better while giving me a kiss on the cheek, and we were off. It seemed as if nothing had happened at all. It's wonderful how better things feel after a kiss on the cheek. Especially if it's from mom.

My frequenting of Wal-Mart continued through my childhood and into my teens. It grew significantly once I acquired my driver's license when Wal-Mart trips became a steady routine. I could not get over how people could shop anywhere else, Wal-Mart's prices were so incredible. My obsession peaked, though, at the age of twenty when I finished the community college and moved on to a real university.

I am positive I'm not alone in stating that college apartment realtors truly pride themselves on financially draining college students. Do they really believe that *every* mommy and daddy can afford to pay for their degree-seeking child's rent and bills and groceries that they can just charge whatever astronomical monthly fee they desire? And the thing of it is, a lot of college apartments are absolute shit. I mean complete trash. I'd rather sleep at a bus depot. If I were homeless I wouldn't live in one of those cesspools. Oh, you can find very nice college apartments, but you could also have a mortgage. They are a vicious people, these college realtors, but college students have to live somewhere, so we'll pay what they tell us, because we don't have a lot of options.

Hence, Wal-Mart. The following statement could very well be a legitimate fact: Wal-Mart's three busiest days of the year are the day after Thanksgiving, the day after Christmas, and college move-in day. Every single college town needs a Wal-Mart. Well, except for maybe those towns with Ivy League type schools where most of the people who attend probably have never set foot inside of a Wal-Mart. My college town, along with its twin city, had one. When I first moved into my college apartment I was at Wal-Mart what seemed an average of five times per day. Couldn't spend enough, couldn't get enough stuff. Never did I shop at a typical grocery store. Subsequently, the more experienced of Wal-Mart shopper I became, the less I frequented. I would say by the time I graduated college I averaged three trips a week. I was good, too . I'm still good. In and out. I'm a model Wal-Mart shopper. I rarely spend time driving around the parking lot trying to find a decent spot. I always say "hello" to the greeter. I always walk on my side of the aisle, never down the middle, or against traffic as some people do. I am very good at quickly finding the shortest check-out line. I place items together on the check-out conveyor in favor of how they will be bagged. Frozen food. Canned goods. Toiletries. Paper items. Delicates such as bread and eggs. I always say "thank you" to the greeter when leaving. And I always, always return my cart to the nearest parking lot cart corral. The average Wal-Mart trip now takes me approximately twenty minutes. Some people dread going to Wal-Mart, and I'll admit, it is too crowded a lot of the time and they never have enough registers open to accommodate the number of shoppers, but attention must not be paid to anyone else in the store, and perhaps you'll find it, as I do, to be a very undemanding experience.

What I mainly came to love about Wal-Mart, other than their unbeatable everyday low prices, was that they were truly the staple of one-stop shopping experiences. I recall one such trip in particular. I went to Wal-Mart to get my oil changed and naturally had time to kill. In this one stop, I was able to get a haircut, purchase contact lenses, some groceries, socks, toiletries, a DVD, and a poster frame. I even put some gas in my car before leaving the parking lot, and then went home. Not only did I save money, I saved gas by not having to go from place to place, but more importantly, I saved time. Time and money—the two most important facets of any typical college student. I tell people to this day that I am fairly confident Wal-Mart played a role in my graduating college. It allowed me to save time to focus on important school matters, and I was able to save the much needed money to help pay for an over-priced apartment. And for that, I am grateful.

Now, for those of you still with me, I am not as naïve as I may be coming off. As mentioned before, Wal-Mart is the world's largest company. Along with that title comes one thing: POWER. I know it, you know it, Wal-Mart knows it. It should come as no surprise that if Wal-Mart were to shut down, if they ceased to be, the earth itself may just stop spinning. There are a large number of companies, vendors, suppliers in this world that if Wal-Mart were to stop doing business with them, they would have no choice but to shut their doors. That is a frightening thought, but a realistic fact. A great number of good, decent people rely, directly and indirectly, on the success of Wal-Mart.

Many things have been said about Wal-Mart over the years, especially since the passing of founder Sam Walton.

"All they do is drive local businesses, the mom and pop shops, right into the ground."

"Wal-Mart is a complete monopoly with nothing but world domination as their goal."

"Their employee benefits are ridiculous and unfair."

"They treat store and distribution center workers like garbage."

Things of this nature. The facts are out there people. Yet I regret to inform you I have not done my homework. One would think the noble thing to do would be to research such a topic before commenting. I don't disagree. However I am just telling you how I feel. Some things, or everything, that we hear about Wal-Mart may be true, I don't know, I've never worked for the company. I know just about as much as any other average Wal-Mart shopper, and like them, I do know I simply go there to save time and money. Again, time and money—the two most important facets of any typical human being. The obvious bottom line is that if you don't like Wal-Mart, don't shop there. Rarely can one go to any Wal-Mart in the country and not find the parking lot manifested with vehicles. Unless, of course, it's three o'clock a.m., which truly is the best time to shop at Wal-Mart.

So, obsessed? Goes without saying. Nevertheless, it was this mild obsession which drove me to make a very significant decision regarding my 2004 spring break destination.

Bentonville, Arkansas.

Oh yes. *The* birthplace of Wal-Mart.

Well what vacation hot spots does one think of when trying to choose a popular spring break getaway? Daytona Beach; Cancun; Panama City; Bentonville, Arkansas. My fascination with this retail giant was so deep that I had to get there and see it all for myself. The first ever Wal-Mart, or Walton's as it was called. I wanted to stand where this little store and tiny business would go on to change the world and revolutionize the shopping experience. And just a side note, I would be remise if I did not mention how I found the northwest corner of Arkansas to be such a prosperous and beautiful part of the country. I would recommend it to anyone. Yet be that as it may, very little did I realize then, how much this trip would end up changing my own little world.

The Fifth Chapter

Embassy Suites Hotel
Rogers, Arkansas
Friday, March 12, 2004
5:47 p.m.

"Hello, room 304."

"Stop fooling around, Kelly, I know what room it is, I just dialed it! Now I've been down here at this manager's reception for almost twenty minutes and I'm already on my second screwdriver. You girls told me you'd meet me down here in five minutes. Where are you?"

"Yeah, I don't think we're coming down, Miles."

"What?! You're going to make me sit down here until 7:30 to eat hors d'oeuvres and booze it up all by myself? Come give me some company, at least one of you."

"Ashley and I really don't feel like it. Why don't you just bring the drinks up to the room?"

"Because I don't want to waste precious drinking time running back and forth between here and the room. Now please just get down here dammit!"

"Nope, sorry."

"Kelly, I swear, if one of you doesn't get ..."

CLICK.

"Hello? Hello? Kelly? HELLO ... shit!"

The Sixth Chapter

Sexual Chocolate

After a couple of meaningless years at the community college, I was accepted at a state university a little over an hour away from my hometown. Yes, the twin-city college town with two Wal-Mart's. It was finally an accomplishment I could be proud of and that would perhaps guide me in some direction. Now, when someone asked me where I was going to school, I didn't have to bow my head and lower my voice like I felt I had to before. It wasn't a completely clear path quite yet, however. I applied for and was accepted under general studies. I had not declared a major because I had yet to stumble upon a subject I passionately enjoyed. God forbid I make one large decision to that point in my life. What in the hell was I gonna do? I'll tell you.

Vegas, baby!

The summer I moved down to the university, and shortly before classes were to begin, two of my roommates and I decided we were going to take a semi-spontaneous trip to Vegas. I say "semi-spontaneous" because it wasn't like we just hopped in the car one day and took off. One of my roommates proposed the idea to me in the parking lot of a Target store (not my choice to be there). I considered it for about eight seconds and thought it was the best idea I had ever heard, and from there we both brought it up to our third roommate who also eagerly obliged. It's amazing the opportunities freedom provides when people do not work for an entire summer and can basically do as they please. The decision was made to drive out the following weekend. The three of us were only twenty years old. Didn't matter. We were driving to Vegas for one sole purpose. Fast food.

The In-n-Out Burger restaurant is briefly mentioned in one of the greatest films ever produced, *The Big Lebowski*.

"He lives in North Hollywood on Radford, near the In-n-Out Burger ..."

"The In-n-Out Burger is on Camrose."

"*Near* the In-n-Out Burger ..."

"Those are good burgers, Walter."

"Shut the fuck up, Donny."

We did some research on the business and the three of us were fascinated by the major popularity of a fast-food joint that had such a limited menu at a small number of locations throughout a tiny geographical area. If memory serves, at the time there were a few locations in Las Vegas, one in Arizona, and the rest in California. The company's refusal to expand eastward and lose quality by becoming a nationwide chain was brilliant. Also, despite the fact we were not twenty-one years old yet, we chose to go to Vegas because, well, it's Vegas, and the town just looked so cool having been stylized in such films as *Ocean's 11*, *Leaving Las Vegas*, and *Swingers*. It seemed like such a different world to us. You'd be hard pressed not to find someone with a good Vegas story under their belt.

In preparation for our little venture, one of my roommates squeezed in as many road-trip themed movies as he could in five days. A short time into our trip, somewhere inside the great vastness of the Missouri Valley, our roommate told us the story of just how a day earlier he had been watching *Easy Rider* and was amazed by what a great film it was, how the three of us were going to be just like Hopper, Fonda, and Nicholson, only not on choppers, and how he was just all into it and so pumped up, when suddenly the end of the film came. **SPOILER ALERT!** The bikers get blown away (my apologies if I just ruined it for anyone). Supposedly my roommate's enthusiasm quickly subsided as he stared blankly at the screen, wide-eyed and mouth open until the final credit rolled. It was not the ending he was expecting and hardly the high note he was seeking for the start of our journey. Nor was it a story my other roommate and I necessarily wanted to hear so prematurely into our trip, or not at all until we had safely returned home.

Nevertheless, twenty-eight straight driving hours later, with tornado alley, the Texas panhandle, New Mexico, Arizona, the mesmerizing beauty and landscape of the southwest we had never seen, and a stop by the Hoover Dam behind us, we found ourselves on the Vegas strip. From the beam of light atop the Luxor pyramid, to the grand fountains at the Bellagio, to the Stratosphere Tower, it was almost too much to take in at one time. The lights, the sounds, the people, the buildings. I like to think it's something everyone may have a chance to experience sometime. Sad part is, after passing all of these luxurious hotels, we had to stay way, way, way down the strip past all of the cool stuff to actually find a hotel which allowed people under the age of twenty-one to check in. There are tens of thousands of hotel rooms in Vegas, but if you're not twenty-one, there are about eight you can check in to. Ah well, I found myself back in Vegas three years later staying at the Bellagio, so it all came full circle.

The following afternoon we took in as much of the strip and hotel walk-thru's as we could. I even wasted some money stopping at an oxygen bar, with all different types of air that were supposed to make me feel ... distinct. The only thing it did was sting my nostrils. I find myself in Vegas and one thing I choose to do is pay nine bucks to breathe. But the moment of truth came shortly thereafter. We found ourselves an In-n-Out Burger which was crowded as hell. We stood in front of the building gazing and smiling, the three of us knowing the trip was going to be worthwhile, even though the hilarity that took place between us on the drive out sort of already made it as such. We all ordered as much food as we thought we could handle. I hesitate to even call it fast food. The burger is still one of the best I've ever had. The food was hot and the service friendly. It was more than we could have hoped for. We sat basically silent while we indulged ourselves; the purpose of our trip had been fulfilled. So after dining, we left Vegas having been there a mere twenty hours, and not surprisingly, the drive home consisted of two more overnight stays because the adrenaline is just never the same heading home, even though home is where your bed is.

My first semester at the university started only days after we returned and it flew by in a blink. Christmas passed just the same, as did second semester. The following summer was a nice break where I lived back home and worked for three months. By my third semester I found myself declared an English major. I mean, I had to choose something. I also found the joy, that semester, of taking the minimal number of credit hours required to be considered a full-time student, all the while spreading those hours out into just three days a week. Goes without saying, and those whom have gone to college will definitely understand, looking back it probably would not have hindered me to have perhaps taken a few more hours per semester. The best part is I never saved me from myself. My final two college semesters I was able to spread those twelve hours into just two days a week. Friday thru Monday weekends, with Wednesday's off to boot. Ah, the familiar shiver of regret. So, with my freshly declared cop-out major at hand, and Writing minor for shits, in came the reading and writing requisites. Damn that word. I wonder how she's doing?

The first day of class for that third semester, on a hot August morning, I was standing outside some random classroom with several other of my English major peeps waiting for someone to come unlock the door. We just stood there as the surrounding classrooms filled up and professors began speaking, each of us exchanging awkward glances because a good seven minutes had passed since we were supposed to start class. That is when someone resembling and dressed like a typical college student came pacing up in between all of us with keys in hand.

"Shit, I thought we all were in another room."

Our awkward glances turned to awkward laughter as our supposed professor unlocked the door. We all shuffled in and sat at desks which were arranged in the shape of a square. Now we could return to our awkward glances. Our professor stood at one end of the square. There was silence while he looked around. He spoke.

"I say 'shit' and 'fuck' a lot. I have my Master's degree and am currently going for my Doctorate. You're going to like me, trust me. I'm the fuckin' shit. Now that I've broken the ice, all you crackers can get over the fact that I'm black."

Interesting approach.

"This is Foundations of Children's Literature, and I should mention I'm also a pervert too. All we're going to do in this class is read children's books such as *Alice in Wonderland*, *The Secret Garden*, *The Cat in the Hat Comes Back*, and discuss how they all relate to sex. I'm one horny bad-ass. I *luuuuvs* the sexual chocolate."

Huh. And we all thought the hallway was awkward. What was going through my mind at that time was not the fact this guy was swearing, using racial slurs, or how he may, and eventually would, become one of the greatest teachers I would ever have, but what was going through my mind was how I had absolutely no clue what "sexual chocolate" meant. I wasn't cool or hip enough. As I stated before, I just wasn't that guy. Actually I'm still not.

I'm just so sheltered and uncultured, and there is constantly new slang entering our society that I just don't attempt to keep up. But *sexual chocolate*? I kept wondering, does this man actually have sexual fantasies about chocolate, and then proceed to act upon those fantasies? Does he get aroused when standing in the supermarket check-out line and spots a Symphony Bar? For all I knew, he gratified himself before, during, and after consuming a bag of Oreos. Double-stuffed. There's a cake out there called "Better Than Sex." Can that name still apply when one actually has sex with it? There's no wrong way to eat a Reese's? I think there is, and I believe this guy may have found it. Hell, you get this guy some Cocoa Puffs and a Yoo-Hoo and he'll be set for the rest of the evening.

I still hope to perhaps one day understand what it actually means.

The Seventh Chapter

Embassy Suites Hotel
Rogers, Arkansas
Friday, March 12, 2004
5:48 p.m.

"That was a mistake," I thought to myself as I hung up the phone with Kelly and walked back to my table in the middle of the reception area. "I guess now the three other chairs will remain empty." I mean, Kelly and Ashley would not even had to of drank, but at least come down and keep me company. Not even that, they could have just sat at the table in silence, perhaps occasionally chucking peanuts at my face. Just something! But nope. I figured I would just sit alone and guzzle screwdrivers for the next hour and a half knowing each sip will drive me further into inebriation resulting in one miserable trek up to St. Louis the following morning.

What did I care?

I was just about to take a seat when I looked down and realized my drink was almost finished. "Dammit," I said under my breath when I looked up to see the drink line was about eight people deep.

"Typical," I heard a voice say just as I was about to start walking to the drink window. I looked down at the table full of women behind me, and locked eyes with the most stunning red-headed girl I had ever seen. She was looking up at me, smiling. The sort of shock, I guess, of her beauty kind of took me back and overwhelmed me a bit. It took me a moment to realize she must have seen my acknowledgment of the drink line and heard my faint swear word that followed.

"Yeah, a pretty typical situation," I said, smiling back. "I'm alone and my drink is empty." Her smile widened. Some silence passed as I tried to think. "Do you need a drink since I'm heading up?" I asked, not quite sure if she was even drinking anything.

"Hmmm...," she pondered, "I'll have what you're having."

"You got it." I walked to the end of the drink line stunned. Random people rarely speak to me, particularly random attractive women. When I got to the back of the line I wanted to look at her again, but I stared straight forward because I figured across the room eye contact would conjure up a mild awkwardness. The line actually went fairly quick because my head was filled with thoughts on how I was inevitably going to burn this bridge.

"What'll it be, sir?" the bartender asked.

"Two screwdrivers."

"That'll be two dollars." I threw the bartender three bucks and walked back to her table.

(Side note: Since that particular Arkansas Embassy Suites is located in a dry county, the hotel is required, by state law I assume, to charge money for alcoholic drinks during their manager's reception, whereas almost every other Embassy Suites in the country provides free alcoholic beverages to their guests. With that being said, I was essentially buying this woman a drink without even having to ask "May I buy you a drink?" Now I realize men buy random women drinks all the time without the women knowing. But I just found it mildly ironic because had I been at any other Embassy, the drinks would have been free, and in my opinion, made the gesture of getting this fine young woman a drink less intimate.)

"Here you go," I said as I handed her the drink.

"Thanks so much," she said, again with that great smile. "Actually, would you mind if I joined you?"

Now I was genuinely stunned.

"Sure, that would be nice." She stood up and left the group of women she had been sitting with and sat in the chair to my right. She was wearing an orange and yellow sundress with pink sandals; very summery, despite it being the middle of March. Her thick auburn-red hair fell past her shoulders and was slightly curled at the end. My goodness was she lovely. I smiled. "My name's Miles," I said as I stuck out my hand.

"Hi, Miles. I'm Raven," she said as our hands met. *What a mystifying name.* "Thank you for getting the drink. I'm here with my mom and some of her friends and it's pretty boring. One of her friends, the woman in the green top right there, is getting married ... again. They're just exchanging gifts and having some drinks, but my mom wanted me to come along. I can remember her friend being around ever since I was little, so I know her pretty well, but I really don't have a lot to talk about with them, you know?"

"I know exactly what you mean. I've been to a ton of bridal parties, and oddly enough, I rarely have anything to say either." Raven laughed and covered her mouth because she had just taken a drink. I was glad she got my sarcasm, but I was praying she would not ask me what I was doing there.

"So are you from around here, Miles, or...?"

I couldn't start the conversation off with a lie, but telling an attractive woman I'm in Arkansas strictly to visit the first Wal-Mart ever? That just screams *NEVER GETS LAID!* But I'm a terrible liar.

"No, I'm from Illinois."

"Oh, cool. I've been to Chicago once. I'd like to get back sometime, very cool city. What brings you to our little state?"

And there it was. I would have preferred almost any other question. *Why are you alone? What's with your nasty facial hair? What's with your regular hair?* Anything except for why I was actually there. "I'm here ... with two friends...," I spoke hesitantly, "because we were in Bentonville today ... taking a tour ... of the first Wal-Mart." I'm sure her mother's friends seemed much more appealing to her at that moment.

"Oh, okay, sure," she said, "I actually talk to a lot of people who come around here for that reason. It's a pretty big attraction."

Whew! She didn't immediately get up and flee. "So you're from around here then?" I asked.

"Yup. I go to school at the University of Arkansas, over in Fayetteville. It's not too far from here. My mom and her friends and I aren't staying at the hotel, we just met here for the get together."

"I see. I'm in school right now as well, on spring break. I'm fairly positive I'm the first person to ever travel to Bentonville, Arkansas for their spring break trip. Please don't consider that bragging. I just realized how pathetic it is as I said it out loud just then. I'm actually traveling with two other people, my friend Kelly and her cousin Ashley. They, however, decided to add to my patheticness and refused to join me down here, hence my sitting alone."

"Awww ... well you're not alone anymore," Raven said. Those words gave me a feeling of pure bliss. "So what are you studying in school?"

"English and Writing. And yes, it's true what you've heard, the constant excitement of that major is almost too much to take."

"I don't know how you do it. I always hated English."

"You are one of many I've heard that from, Raven."

"So do you want to be a teacher?"

"Um, I did," I sputtered out, "but I went a different direction because, to be honest, there really is not one particular subject I'm passionate enough about to devout myself to. English is just sort of a cop-out. And having to deal with parents I don't think I could handle either. So many of them think their children are perfect and can do no wrong, and that bothers me immensely. I strongly admire teachers, but there's just too much politics. Those are a few reasons among many others I suppose."

"Well I'm definitely not perfect," Raven said, staring down at her drink. "So what are you going to do if you're not gonna teach? You could always teach college ... no parents there."

"You know I would really love to teach college. Teaching in that setting seems more laid back and professors are allowed to just do their own thing. But a person needs at least a Master's degree and preferably a Doctorate to teach college, and I don't have near the passion for English to pursue either one of those degrees. In a perfect world, what I would ideally like to do is write a book. But again, a lack of passion, or ambition I should say...." I started to feel as if I was talking but not really saying anything. "This has to be boring you, Raven. Please, tell me what you're in school for."

"I'm not bored, Miles. If I was I wouldn't stay." I was relieved when she said that, despite the fact I had seen her glance at her watch moments earlier. "I'm studying interior design at the moment. I've changed my major like five times, but I think I have finally found something I actually enjoy."

"I can definitely relate. I started off wanting to go into English, at a community college no less, only to change my major a half-dozen or so times, just to end up where I started almost three years later. I could have been applying to Master's school right now if I would have just stuck with my first choice."

"Nothing wrong with community college, Miles." I had no comment. "I could go for another drink. You? I doubt my mom and her friends even noticed I left the table."

"Sure, I'll go get us a couple more." I took Raven's glass and headed up to the drink line. I could not believe how well things were going. Yes, she may have looked at her watch once or twice, and I may have felt a certain lack of confidence in entertainingly holding up my end of the conversation, but something just felt right, even though I thought I was definitely talking too much. I really do need to learn when to shut the hell up. I was probably suffocating the poor girl to some extent, but she was simply easy to talk to. I love women who can hold a good conversation. As the bartender was pouring our drinks, I smiled as I realized the irony that if Kelly and Ashley had come down, Raven would have just been another random girl I noticed in a room, having never spoken a word to one another.

I turned around from the drink window and noticed Raven was not at my table, and the table occupying her mother and friends was empty as well. I slowly walked back, scanning the room as best I could for Raven's flowing red hair. Nothing. I plopped myself back in my chair. Two drinks, one person. It was just as well. I should have figured a conversation with an enjoyable woman would only be brief until she wised up and disappeared.

A bit of paranoia and fear set in as I thought, "Maybe it never happened. I probably imagined the whole damn thing. There was no group of women. No Raven. No red hair. Has my loneliness and lack of physical female contact gotten so deep that I'm having conversations with imaginary people? What if I'm schizophrenic? Am I even in Arkansas? Oh God! I'm losing my mind! I'M ... "

"Miles?"

I looked up with a panic-stricken expression to find Raven's calming face looking down at me. She did exist. Perhaps I am a bit more of a hypochondriac than a schizoid. "I'm sorry, I was in the lobby with my mom and her friends. They're gonna take off, but I told them I was going to stay a little longer. You don't mind, do you?" That's when I went back to thinking I was a basket case. *She actually wanted to stay?*

"Absolutely not. I am really having a nice time. Hope you don't mind another screwdriver," I said as I placed the drink in front of her as she joined me once again.

The Voice of Reason: The Title

"*Girl-Shaped Shadows*?? What the hell kind of a title is that, Miles? I say with great confidence the only shadows you see that are in the shape of a female body are those of the innocent women you stalk. Shadows on the window, no doubt?"

"Ha! That's laughable. I may be a fairly desperate man, but I would never resort to stalking or spying on women."

"Laughable, huh? You should be counting your blessings there aren't numerous restraining orders out on your creepy ass. I'm sure you'll be laughing hysterically when the time comes that you won't be able to walk a mere ten feet in any direction without being within one-hundred yards of someone you shouldn't."

"Must you find it necessary to mock and berate the book's title? It is what it is."

"Well I do know what it isn't. Appropriate. Does the title not come off as a bit ... pedophilic? I mean, *girl*-shaped shadows. May give some people the wrong impression."

"What kind of a person are you? Where is your mind? It's not meant to be like that ... at all!! I simply find the title to be unique, maybe a bit provocative. The title is crucial. It has to be catching. Again, people can take from it what they choose."

"Indeed, Miles, and I'm choosing to take it as a distasteful title. And it's a hyphenate no less! How about something like *Shadows of Women* or *The Female Outline,* or simply *Miles To Go.*"

"I'm sorry, *The Female Outline*? This is not a book of tracings, or of sketches!"

"Or, hey, how about *Shadows on the Window,* like I mentioned before?"

"Okay, actually, that's not too bad. Ughhh ... I'm sticking with the girl shapes, dammit! Let come of it what will."

"Jeez, calm down. I'm just trying to give you suggestions here, Miles. And aren't you afraid the title may not appeal much to men? You're lucky you put an actual outline of a female body on the cover, which may draw some male attention, because I don't think the title alone is going to do it. You may as well have a shirtless Fabio pictured on the cover. And speaking of pictures, did a headless person choose the author's photo? It's completely unprofessional! And what or whom are you waving at? Or are you waving goodbye to your dignity? *Bye-bye self-respect. See ya' later any chance of getting a chick. Adios successful future!* Oh, and *Bravo!* on the book's description. *Meet them both....* No one wants to meet you! You really need to get it through your thick skull that a miniscule number of people are interested in this thing. A minimal amount."

"Are you finished?"

"Hey, if you're not going to consider my suggestions, then hell with ya'. I'll just go back to doing what I enjoy most, berating your 'novel' and trying to persuade you that you need to stop writing before you kill any more trees—a very green suggestion you should strongly ponder. Let me put it to you this way, Miles. You're better off to start drinking and becoming a raging alcoholic. Don't a lot of writers do that? I mean, trying to make yourself believe you've written seven chapters in just a small number of pages? Look at this current chapter alone, for example! This is not the beginnings of a novel. This is the beginnings of a practical joke you're unknowingly playing on yourself, but you're too proud and stubborn to realize it. You've clearly lost all sense of self-respect, dignity, and hope. You have nothing else to lose. And when you have nothing else to lose, you have nothing else to fear."

"Then if I have nothing to fear, why not attempt to give it a shot? You just contradicted yourself if I understand the meaning of the word. If you're going to continually demean my efforts here the least you can do is be consistent."

"Oh, don't doubt for a second there is not any fear, Miles. There's fear. Fear that you'll never complete this thing. Fear that it will never get published. The fear of people, one, not reading it, and two, if they do read it, they'll hate themselves afterwards. Readers are going to experience deeply passionate regret for attempting to read this. Look at it this way. If you don't write this book, you'll never find out that people despise it. However, if you do write it, you will most certainly find out people despise it. It's a double-edged sword.

Yet in your case, I fully realize that you hope the very pen you write with will prove to be mightier than that sword, but I'm here to convince you it won't. You'll be destroyed by a Bic. Well played! People rarely see what's right in front of them. Just look at this writing, Miles, it has very little structure thus far. What is it you're actually trying to do here? Just weave random antidotes into the middle of some larger overlying story?"

"Well yeah, actually, that's exactly what I am trying to do. More or less."

"I'd say less. But please, continue. Let's see how further down this literary slippery slope you can slide. Wow, that was some jazzy alliteration! There's your consistency."

The Ninth Chapter

Negotiations

William Shatner. Yes, *that* William Shatner. You ever negotiated with him? I don't mean personally. I mean, if you have, that's amazing. No, what I'm talking about is negotiation via the Priceline.com website. I entered my twenty-first year in early 2003 accompanied with a handsome benefits package. I could now legally purchase and consume alcohol. I could rent a car with ease. I could finally bid money on a hotel room via Priceline.com. Since then, that website has been both a financial blessing, and a burden. More on that later.

Yes, one could safely say it was around this time that Priceline.com became almost as big of an obsession for me as Wal-Mart. The possibility of getting a four-star hotel at a two-star price? I simply couldn't fathom it. I can name my own price and some really classy hotel may actually say, "Yes, you can stay with us, Mr. Truckenbrod." *Whoa*. To the folks over at Visa and MasterCard: start raising those credit limits, because I'm gonna be taking advantage!

The mere fact alone that I could put in, for example, a $60 bid and get a room at the four-diamond Chicago Hilton on Michigan Avenue wasn't the only driving force. There are another three words in my repertoire: I. LOVE. HOTELS. Two major obsessions—hotels and Wal-Mart—with Priceline.com being a subsidiary addiction. The taller the hotel, the better, too. Let's not forget that. The request for a high floor room is given immediately upon check-in if I am staying at a tall hotel. I suppose it's safe to say tall buildings in general fascinate me. Architecture and such. I imagine a psychiatrist could have a field day with that fixation. I'd be a dream patient.

Hotels, in my humble opinion, make a trip. Sure, one can be on vacation with gorgeous surroundings and beautiful weather, but to then return to a dilapidated hotel? Sort of kills the mood. "Well it's just a place to sleep," I hear a lot. "I don't need all those fancy amenities." Okay, fine. That is where the beauty of Priceline comes in. Instead of paying $80 per night at the Comfort Inn five blocks away from the beach, why not bid that same amount of money on a beach front resort and see what happens? Perhaps as I did, you will get that Hilton resort right on Myrtle Beach. One need not dig too deep into their pockets to stay in the lap of luxury, my friends. Just don't repeatedly abuse the privilege. Repeatedly abuse ... just as I began doing around the later part of 2003 into 2004 and so forth.

Throughout college I would frequent Priceline.com, usually late at night and often with alcohol floating my liver, and put in an insanely low hotel bid, typically in the Chicagoland area. I always presumed a hotel at whatever particular star-rating I bid on would never accept such a low price. I was surprisingly mistaken more often than not. Two or three days later, off I would go. Over the years I found myself, by myself, at a plethora of random cities and hotels as a result of an accepted bid.

The Conrad—Chicago, IL
The Doubletree—Schaumburg, IL
Hilton Garden Inn—Chicago, IL
The Radisson—St. Louis, MO
The Renaissance—Springfield, IL
The Millennium Knickerbocker Hotel—Chicago, IL
Indian Lakes Hilton—Bloomingdale, IL
The Radisson—Indianapolis, IN
Hyatt Regency—Chicago, IL
The Sheraton—Chicago, IL
... to name a few.

One such "mini-getaway" as I called them took me to the Hilton Suites in Oakbrook Terrace, Illinois. Please keep in mind I had just returned from spring break not even a week prior which found myself, along with Kelly and Ashley, with stop over's in Memphis, Tennessee; Bentonville, Arkansas; and St. Louis, Missouri, so naturally I decided the best thing to do would be to get away ... again. Oh, indeed, it was great getting these hotels at such fantastic prices, but I rarely ever considered the added expenses which accompanied these meaningless getaways. Gas to and from. Wear and tear on my vehicle. Food and alcohol. Entertainment. It all rapidly adds up. Damn, when I look back ... just so much shame.

I checked into my Hilton suite, set my bag on the bed, admired the size of the room, and asked myself as I always did, "Okay, what now?" The unsettling truth that these little getaways of mine served absolutely no point would not occur to me until years and a heap of debt later. It's no wonder I was never getting laid, I was always by myself in hotel rooms, or at Wal-Mart. As routine would have it, I left my room shortly thereafter and checked out the rest of the hotel, pool area, etc. Sometimes I would enjoy a drink at the bar. I went to these hotels and basically roamed about, utilized the pool and hot tub, and drove around whatever congested suburb the hotel happened to be in. I cannot stress enough the lack of purpose or intent I rationalized myself into believing these one-night getaways had.

Well I can always go see a movie. Alright. I took advantage of the Hilton's business center internet access to find out what was playing when and where. *Eternal Sunshine of the Spotless Mind* at the AMC. I am big fan of Jim Carrey in both comedic and dramatic roles. I drove to the theater in what should have only taken me twenty minutes, but took me a solid forty-five because of all the traffic and stop lights. Needless to say I was mildly pissed off when I walked into the theater. It was surprisingly empty, so I chose a seat location directly in the center.

This is nice.

The previews ran quite a while, which I didn't mind because I actually enjoy them. As the film started, I was all situated and comfortable, and the experience was terrific, for about ten minutes. That is when I noticed the dark figures of two people enter the theater and stop. They were both looking at all of the empty seats and pointing. I could clearly hear the tense negotiation between them as to where the best place to sit would be. It's not difficult to imagine where this is going. I watched them as they approached, getting closer, both their arms full of movie theater garbage. And inevitably, out of all of the empty seats in the entire freakin' theater, a man, two-hundred years old, and his decaying carcass of a wife chose two seats right next to mine, with a one-seat buffer in between myself and the man corpse, whom I'm sure had just come from his Wal-Mart greeter job.

Now I don't mean any disrespect or such to the elder community, but they were already loud entering the theater, and to choose two seats right next to the *only* person there? Come on! In hindsight, I should have just gotten up and moved, but I didn't want to be blatantly rude. And as soon as they were settled, the old man cleared his throat in such a manner which omitted sounds I didn't even know were humanly possible. Then he started in on the popcorn. Shoving handful after wrinkly old handful of that shit into his mouth. However, it wasn't just an up and down motion. Popcorn to mouth. Popcorn to mouth. No. He had like this routine. He would heave popcorn into his mouth, take a giant slurp of his beverage, which I'm confident was spiked with Metamucil or some regulatory substance, then wipe his hand and mouth with a napkin, then repeat as such. For those unaware, poorly made cheap napkins are basically just soft paper, and when cleaning a hand that has over the years turned completely into leather, it forms quite a loud sound in an unpopulated theater.

I struggled to hear the film.

So I tried a number of common gestures. I cleared *my* throat for an over-extended amount of time. But alas I was no competition for this man's throat clearing capabilities. I over-dramatically shifted in my seat several times in a short period. Nothing. I finally turned my head to the right and just stared at this man, screaming at him with my inner monologue. *HOW AND WHY ARE YOU SO OLD? CLEAN YOUR HANDS ONLY ONCE WHEN YOU ARE FINISHED WITH THE DAMN POPCORN!* If I'm indulging in, let's say, a half-rack of barbeque spare ribs, I don't clean my fingers with a moist towelette after every bite! What's the point? Well my silent screaming must have been affective, and I'm not quite certain if he actually perished right there in the theater, but shortly thereafter I didn't hear another sound from him for the remainder of the film.

Despite the elder folk setback, I returned to my hotel extremely pleased with what I had just seen. That screenwriter Charlie Kaufman is truly a gifted mind. I can only dream to write as well and original as he does. Seeing as I had eaten before the movie, I figured the best thing to do would be to wind down with a relaxing soak in the hot tub. I changed into my suit and headed down to the pool, but as I approached, I could see four heads basking in the hot tub. I swiped my key card and entered the pool area. I immediately took notice of a family of four enjoying the hot tub I was longing to be in. I quickly looked away and walked past, forced to settle on the regular pool, which was empty.

How long are they going to be in there? I don't want to be in this pool very long! I submerged myself under water for a minute and enjoyed what I heard. Silence. I popped my head back above the water and looked up as I wiped off my face. All I could see through the glass above were stars against the black on a cloudless night, along with the adjacent Oakbrook Terrace Tower aiming for the sky. It was quite a sight. A rather genuine, yet humbling feeling of insignificance came over me. I just felt so tiny looking up at space from that pool. So I diverted my attention elsewhere. Then ...

BOOM!

I glanced over to the hot tub and noticed the family had gotten out. I instantly started to head for the pool stairs. As I climbed up the stairs, I looked to my left, and slow motion seemed to set in. The husband, standing in front of his family, slowly turned away to ultimately reveal his goddess of a trophy wife drying herself off. My eyes widened and my jaw dropped. *How I need to look away.* I forced myself to look down at my protruding gut as I walked toward the hot tub. The only thing I made sure to do was to sit down in the hot tub to where I could get a clear vantage point of her. Thank goodness the blowers were still on because by that point I was finding it difficult to hide my excitement.

This incredible female could not have been more than twenty-five years young. And that body ... forget about it. Incredible. The father was playing with his two daughters in the pool as my disgusting self just sulked, full on creepily staring at his wife as she lay back in her chair, watching her family. How did this dude snag her up? I'm assuming not by sitting alone in a hotel hot tub inappropriately staring at her.

Then, as I was mulling over all of the advancements I would like to make towards her, the blowers shut off. It sort of took me by surprise. I looked around the hot tub, perplexed. Perhaps my abundance of body hair had clogged the motor. That is when I heard a voice.

"Would you like me to turn the blowers back on so you don't have to get out?"

It was the soothing voice of the young mother of two, who had already started to get up from her chair. I quickly shot a glance to her husband who was preoccupied with his daughters. "Sure," I mustered up, "I'd appreciate that." I felt lucky I was able to get that out coherently, because her saying the word "blower" almost proved too much.

I could not help but just stare at her as she crossed the pool area. That tight little white bikini, teasing me. Taunting me. Looking at me saying, "Hey ... you ... doucher in the hot tub. You will never, ever have anything like this. You should try being a bikini. It's amazing!"

"Yeah, well fuck off bikini!"

My God. Is this what it's come to? Having an imaginary conversation with an article of clothing. Does it get any more wretched? Well by the time the depression started to sink in the blowers were back on and white bikini was walking back to her chair. "Thanks," I said. She smiled and sat back down. At that point I really just wanted to go back to my room and cry myself to sleep, knowing that if I were to ever get laid it certainly would not be with a woman like her. However, it would have been rude of me to up and leave after she had so kindly turned the jets back on for me. Heaven forbid I try striking up a conversation with her in the meantime. I just continued to pine in that hot tub, silent, still bearing that feeling of insignificance.

I looked over to the pool, and thought, "Is what I am seeing in front of me, a father playing with his two children as his wife looks on, is what I am seeing genuine happiness? A *true* life? If it is, I don't think I will ever get there."

I surely don't.

The Tenth Chapter

Embassy Suites Hotel
Rogers, Arkansas
Friday, March 12, 2004
7:00 p.m.

An hour and almost three screwdrivers had come and gone as I glanced at my watch to find it was seven o'clock. Raven and I, in the most innocent way, had really been enjoying each other. I tend to meet people often on my little travels, a hotel or restaurant bar is usually involved, but things seemed different this time. I am not sure if it was that my confidence had been boosted because Raven voluntarily asked to sit with me, or if I was simply overwhelmed by how classy she was and how well she presented herself. I was deeply interested in everything she had to say, while she paid attention and seemed to truly listen when I spoke. I often tend not to meet women well. I rarely know what to say after the standard introductions. So the fact this was going so well really made chatting with her that much more enjoyable.

"Boy, what time is it, Miles?" Raven asked. She had obviously noticed me glance at my watch.

"Seven o'clock. That hour *flew* by!"

"No kidding. I don't think I've ever enjoyed vodka this much." I hoped she had meant because I was involved with the drinking, but it's hard telling.

"Yes, the drinks are working, which is good."

"Yes they are, also meaning I have to go pee," Raven said, scrunching her face as if she was embarrassed to say that word in front of me.

"You know, I kinda really gotta go, too. Then I'll go and get us a couple more drinks and we'll meet back here in a few."

"Sounds like a plan, Miles." Raven took one last drink to finish it off and set her cup back down on the table. She started walking to the restrooms as I gathered up our two cups.

I walked into the restroom and took a deep, relaxing breath. I was upwards of six screwdrivers deep at that point and wanted to make sure I remained focused and composed. There was only one urinal open as I walked up. A few seconds later I heard a deep voice.

"Long day?"

I didn't even look to my right to acknowledge the man standing next to me. Having a brief chat with a complete stranger while I'm relieving myself and staring down at a urinal cake is not the most appealing conversation setting.

"Well ... you know," I said, hoping to come off as uninterested in conversing.

"I feel ya'. These days is long and life is short, I say. Not quite sure how that works."

"Nope."

"Seems like the only time life stands still is when you're takin' a piss. One of the few moments durin' the day you stop and stand still for a period of time."

Unique concept. "Huh. Never thought about it that way."

"Yep," the stranger said as he flushed. I waited until he left before I went to wash my hands. Yet what he said kind of got to me. To be able to have a mildly philosophical thought on something as obligatory as urination sort of fascinated me. It's something that most of us find to be an inconvenience. I was a bit envious of him that I was never prone to think deeper about random, everyday things, and I was actually sort of regretful I was not friendlier to him, because who knows what else he may have had to say. I washed my hands and walked back to the drink window.

"Two screwdrivers please."

"Coming right up."

I turned my head back around as I was leaning on the counter waiting for the drinks and noticed a man and a woman sitting in the exact same chairs Raven and I had just been occupying. A bewildered look came across my face, more so because it appeared neither was drinking a single beverage between them. It is called a cocktail hour for a reason, so at least get a soda or something. I turned my head back around and looked down at our drinks, then looked back up at the bartender with a skewed face. I grabbed the drinks and started to walk away.

"Excuse me, sir? Sir?" I turned around. "That'll be two dollars."

"Oh yeah, sorry," I said walking back to the window, still confused. I set the drinks back down and reached in my pocket. "Here."

I turned around a second time and noticed Raven's hand waving at me from a couch that was outside the reception area. I nodded my head and smiled as I proceeded to the couch. I took a sip of my drink and handed Raven hers. "One for you. So I take it you noticed our seats were occupado."

"Yeah, I came out of the restroom and was like 'What the hell?' I guess we did leave the table completely empty though. This is more comfy anyway." She had her legs crossed and her left arm draped over the back of the couch. She would occasionally run her fingers through her hair which was just about the best thing in the world at that time. I took another sip of my drink as I tried, quite hard actually, not to get caught admiring her, which probably made it even more obvious. "You know, Miles, if I were you, I wouldn't shove your thoughts about writing a book to the wayside. I think if someone has just an inkling of passion to do something they should try their hardest to do it. Even if you set out and don't accomplish something, that does not mean it was a failure, or nothing was gained from it. Anything worth doing is never easy. Believe me, I know. Getting the money together for college was extremely daunting, but I did what I had to do. That's a conversation for a whole other cocktail hour though."

Raven looked down at her drink while she brushed some hair behind her ear. She must have said something that struck a nerve within her. She was silent for several moments, which was creating a mild awkwardness that I obviously had no idea how to overcome. Then, absurd as it was at that moment, one of Jerry Seinfeld's lines from his television show popped into my head, so I just blurted it out.

"You know, you can't tell by looking at me, but I can run *really* fast!"

Raven looked up and started laughing. "Thanks, Jerry."

"You watch *Seinfeld* I see," Raven said, still giggling.

"Oh yes, for years. You caught that, huh?"

"Yep, it's one of the few shows I watch when I actually do watch television. I try not to get hooked on TV too much. Basically nothing on but reality garbage anyway."

"I hear ya'. If you enjoy *Seinfeld*, then you'd probably love *Curb Your Enthusiasm* on HB...." I was interrupted by the ring of Raven's cell phone. She took the phone out of her purse, glanced at it, and sighed.

"Ughhh ... excuse me, Miles. It's my step-dad." Raven answered the phone and walked a few feet away. She seemed flustered as she spoke, her voice progressively rising. I took some more sips from my drink and looked around at all the people in the reception area filling up the line for one more drink, as it was nearing 7:30 ... closing time. Raven came back a minute later. "Well my step-father is waiting outside for me. Apparently my mom got home and told him to come pick me up, seeing as she drank too much to drive. I hate to end things so abruptly."

"No, not at all, I understand. I should get back up to my room anyway. If my two friends downed that bottle of wine like they threatened, I'm probably locked out of my room. I'll walk out with you though."

I sat my drink on an end table and the two of us started walking to the lobby. We didn't say anything to each other. Raven then suddenly stopped a few feet from the lobby doors. She turned.

"You know, Miles, I am just ... really happy that I met you. You're a good listener, which is rare."

"Really? Well thank you, Raven. I kind of feel like I was the one doing most of the talking."

"You weren't. Thank you so much for the drinks by the way. That was sweet."

"My pleasure. I am really glad you decided to join me at my table. You know ... hang on just a sec." I turned and walked over to the front desk and asked for a pen and paper. And on Embassy Suites stationary I wrote down my first name, cell number, and e-mail address. This is something I never do. Like, ever. But it just felt right that time. So in one of my ballsiest moves, I rushed back over to Raven and handed her the paper. "Here, Raven. Just in case you find yourself back in Chicago some time." Raven held the piece of paper and stared at it for a moment. She looked up.

"I hope I do sometime soon. It was nice meeting you, Mr. Miles." Raven stuck out her right hand.

"You as well, Ms. Raven." I took her hand and held it for a moment. Raven smiled, looked at me and slowly blinked, then turned around and walked out of the sliding doors, the sound of her sandals fading, until she was gone.

I looked down at my hand and was really not surprised to find it empty. No exchange. No number. No e-mail. All I had was a first name, and the memory of that gorgeous red hair. Maybe she would call me one day, but I knew the truth. I was just someone to talk with over drinks. A convenience. But I was so thrilled about meeting her and how well we got along that the notion I would never hear from her again didn't bother me too much. I gave the front desk lady a grin as I turned back toward the elevators. What a reception.

I could hear Kelly and Ashley being a little too loud as I approached our room. I unlocked the door and walked into the bedroom to find them jumping up and down on the beds, an empty bottle of wine laid sideways on the night stand.

I simply looked at the both of them, gave half a grin and shook my head. I never told them a thing.

The following night the three of us found ourselves at the Embassy Suites in the St. Louis Landing. And again, Kelly and Ashley refused to join me at the cocktail hour, so I sat alone, that time for the entire two hours. But at least the drinks were free.

The F Word

Three consonants and one vowel make up one of the most widely used, controversial, degrading, harshest, but albeit entertaining words in the English language. An F. U. C. and K. This small word can have massive effects. It gets children grounded. Adults fired. It is bleeped out and pixilated on television. People scream and moan the word in bed. It's said under the breath in frustration. It's yelled in anger. It's said with a smile during laughter. It is spoken sharply as an insult. It is a word amongst words. Many people despise it, and others take much joy in saying it. And some, well, have never said it at all, which makes it one of the most, if not *the* most fascinating word we have the privilege, or not, of choosing to say.

My two favorite stand-up comedians are Jerry Seinfeld and Chris Rock. Mr. Seinfeld is proud of the fact he does not use swear words or vulgarity in his comedy to garner a laugh. Mr. Rock, on the other hand, relishes in it. I find them both equally hilarious. Some people may feel that offensiveness and crudeness is a cop-out, or used simply for shock value to get people to laugh, and that clean comedy is more difficult to accomplish. All it simply comes down to is individual taste, and what kind of language people choose to use. The same vulgarity that makes one person laugh out loud can make another person run to the confessional clutching a rosary for simply overhearing it. It's all a matter of taste. Does swearing make someone a bad person? Of course not. Does choosing not to swear necessarily make someone good? I don't think so. Some words can just cut deep, but how deep, is all up to the individual.

One of the greatest comedies of all time, in my humble opinion, *Planes, Trains & Automobiles*, is rated R. It could very easily have been rated PG-13 if not for a single scene that lasts merely one minute. Steve Martin's character, Neil Page, uses the word "fucking" eighteen times within a sixty second period as he yells at a rental car agent. It is a memorable scene that has turned into a classic over time despite the crude language. I have a grandmother who would cry laughing during that scene, yet I have not one memory of her ever uttering the word out loud. I suppose the old cliché is true. It's not the word, but rather how it's used.

If you have miraculously read to this point, you've noticed the F word scattered throughout some pages thus far. And to be honest, yes, it has been a moral dilemma for me. I'll admit I do enjoy using the word, but I am very good at controlling the use of it as well. I never say it in front of my mother, grandparents, or most relatives for that matter. I occasionally use the word in front of my father, but that is just because after the first time I said it in front of him, he questioned why it took me so long to do so. Generally speaking, I rarely use the word other than around friends. But it truly is just an enjoyable word to say.

However, I did wrestle with the notion of using the word in this book at all. As much as I hate to say this, a part of me feels guilty because I know certain people will be reading this, and a certain audience could easily be offended or upset reading such language. But then I think, the book starts off talking about strippers, so if certain people have gotten this far, perhaps they have come to expect this type of poor quality and decision making from me. And remember, I am not writing to a certain audience, so with that, the guilt simply turns to mischievous fun.

To get to where I am going with this, I was leaving the barber shop one particular afternoon, fresh from getting my ridiculous hair trimmed, thus making the shape of my head look all the more like a cube. I was driving behind an old, beat up conversion van down a residential street not too far away from my place. I was minding my own business, jamming to Dave Matthews Band, when the van approached a yield sign. I slowed down as the van did, which proceeded to make a left turn at the intersection. I followed suit seconds later. About ten yards down the road the van slowed down again and started to veer to the right. I was following not too far behind, and assumed, as I think most drivers would, that the van was going to park on the right side of the road. So I kept on going, still jamming, when all of a sudden the van makes a huge left turn as if wanting to pull into one of the driveways on the left side of the street. I had to slam on my brakes, ultimately at the same time the van driver slammed on theirs, because I came within feet of side-swiping that old van.

As the van horn blared, I took a deep breath. I avoided a close one. Thank God. I turned my music down. It was about this time I looked back at the van to notice the driver side door opening. From within the confines of the poorly upholstered bucket driver's seat crawled out a generously proportioned woman wearing rather unfortunate clothing and missing some pretty important teeth. Even the most basic of hygiene practices seemed to have eluded her. I had both hands on top of the steering wheel, and peered forth as this raging woman ... well ...

WHERE THE FUCK'D YOU LEARN HOW TO DRIVE YOU FUCKIN' LOSER?? CAN'T YOU SEE I GOT THREE KIDS IN THIS FUCKIN' VAN?? LEARN HOW TO FUCKIN' DRIVE YOU PIECE A SHIT MOTHA FUCKA!!

Now I'm no parent, but the choice of words this woman used seemed ... unsuitable at best to use in front of her little ones, all of whom I'm sure just seconds earlier were begging to know who their respective fathers were. It wasn't spectacle enough to blast her horn for an unprecedented amount of time in this quiet neighborhood, but to take the time and effort to verbally bash me and my driving skills in the middle of the street? I must admit I was kind of impressed. More so for the fact that she found me to be such a predominate Mo Fo that she completely dropped the –er off the ends of both words and replaced them with an –a.

Motha Fucka.

To have oodles of time to stop and ruthlessly scream at strangers must be a luxury us descent folks can only imagine. My only hope is that this woman pulled into her driveway, received the monthly government stipend you and I pay for, and bought something nice for those three children she permanently terrified and psychologically wounded.

The Twelfth Chapter

The Voice of Reason: Caucasian

"Son of a bitch! I just don't understand, Miles. Where to begin? There are so many things wrong with this so-called attempt at a novel it's hard to even pinpoint and dissect. The previous chapter alone, Lord only knows what a significant chunk of audience you just lost, granted there is an audience for what you're trying to do here. You really think elder family members are going to enjoy that type of language? *Any* family members? It's in poor enough taste alone you begin the book talking about strippers and such that you also feel the need to pepper these pages with profanity and then devote an entire chapter to the subject? I feel I just keep repeating myself with you and you refuse to take the hint. You really should have more aptly prepared beforehand with this book instead of just sitting down and basically free-writing and producing the garbage you have so far. I don't really even feel bad for you. I mean this is moronic."

"God I need a drink."

"Indeed, there's the solution. Drown your literary aspirations in an up-teen number of White Russians, or Caucasians as you so callously refer to them. Go sit in a bar and get wasted and annoy people when what you really should be doing is looking back at these chapters you've written and finding ways of improving them. Or, better yet, abandon everything you have written so far and start anew—this time with outlines, and character descriptions, and attractive settings, and dare I say ... AN INTERESTING FUCKING PLOT!! Great, now you've got *me* swearing. Just go to the bar and get the hell outta here!"

I may as well go to the bar. Hell, it's a Thursday and payday, might as well go contribute to the lesser good. I think I'll walk down to the Brickhouse. Best Caucasian in town.

FOUR MINUTES LATER ...

"Miles!" Kyle the bartender bellows with a smile as I open the bar's front door. I return a smile and sit at the almost empty bar. "Let me guess. Either a Blue Moon or a White Russian?"

"Caucasian it'll be, buddy."

"*Big Lebowski* reference. I like that. So what brings you in so early this afternoon?"

"Well I took half of a vacation day today with all good intentions of sitting outside, enjoying the cool weather and getting some writing done. But alas I find myself here. As usual."

There is almost nothing as disappointing than a poorly made White Russian. Too much cream. Too much Kahlua. Not enough vodka. It can almost ruin a perfectly nice evening. Kyle has yet to disappoint.

"Still chipping away at that book, are we?" Kyle asks as he places a napkin in front of me and sets a perfectly tinted White Russian on top. Two straws.

"Thank you, sir. Yeah, that flippin' book! Not ten minutes ago I *was* sitting on my front porch with the best of intentions, but this other character in the book has really started to get to me. He's a pretty big downer and just rips into me constantly."

"Huh. So let me get this straight. A character, in *your* book, that *you've* created and written, has you, *the author,* somewhat depressed?"

"Well I wouldn't say I 'created' him, per say. He's kind of just there and interjects every so often."

"So this character is a male? Don't you sort of have the ability to control what this character says?"

"Well, to be honest, Kyle, it just so happens I'm starting to agree with some of the things he has to say. He's more or less a realist, kind of like me."

"All due respect, Miles, but this has got 'schizoid' written all over it. Basically this other character is you."

"No, this other character's a prick!"

"Well ... "

"Hey-oh!" I belt out as I point to Kyle while he's laughing.

"Miles, I don't know a lot about writing or character development or what have you, and I know you don't really favor talking much about this book of yours. All you have really told me about it is the title and that the main character's name is Miles. Now, just from what I see before me, instead of sitting at home writing, you're sitting at a bar bitching about a character that *you* have created who is brutally honest. Maybe instead of complaining about this character, you should listen to what he has to say."

I take a couple of drinks from my glass, turn my head, and stare out the bar's windows for several moments. I am thinking that my good friend Kyle is completely correct. Instead of dismissing this other character that I have taken the time to write and you have so graciously taken the time to read, perhaps I should embrace him. I mean, are you, the reader, not mildly curious where this other character is coming from? Even I, the author, am beginning to think it's getting a bit creepy to just interweave vague literary opinions and verbal assaults here and there. Or could it be that I am wrong entirely? Perhaps you're primary wonderment is regarding the random short (and I do mean short) stories that may seem to have a partial bearing on something, but are basically interrupting the flow of a greater story that you have more or less loss interest in or haven't even concerned yourself with. Yet having said that, I now feel it's getting time for this other character and I to have a genuine conversation and perhaps try to gain some perspective of what is really happening here, and where one another is coming from, because I do not foresee myself writing him out. He is, after all, the voice of reason.

"Kyle, my good man," I say as I lay a bill down on the bar, "here's a ten. You may have just changed the entire course of my writing, and for that, you're going in the book."

"Well I want some royalties then."

"I would agree to that but there probably won't be any. Isn't it amazing what a little talk over a drink can do?"

"Don't tell me you're not finishing your drink, Miles!"

"Kyle, you are a gentleman and a scholar, but I need to get back home and write."

"Before you leave, can't you just tell me a little something about the book? I mean, what's it even about?"

I smile. "It's about some chick and some dude."

"How very vague, thank you, Miles." I leave my barstool and head for the door. Kyle yells, "Hey, wait a minute. What am I going to be doing in the book?"

I turn back around.

"Everything you just did."

The Thirteenth Chapter

Hello Bottom

I remember with great fondness my first experience at an Embassy Suites Hotel. It was in the early nineties at the Embassy Suites in Des Moines, Iowa. I was fairly young at the time and remember being somewhat overwhelmed because I had never really seen anything like it. The wide open atrium, that when I looked up I could see people walking around every floor, and that ceiling which was so high up. Glass elevators on either side of the lobby were in constant motion. Our hotel room, which seemed so large, with a mini-fridge, chairs and couches, two televisions, and an entirely separate bedroom. I would slowly approach the atrium balcony outside our room and gaze down at all of the people and families, wondering where they all might be from.

Later in the evening, I felt like pretty hot stuff during the manager's reception going up to the bartender and ordering a kitty cocktail, with two cherries on a tiny plastic sword. Then came the next morning with the cook-to-order breakfast. Forget about it. My father told me the cooks would make me almost anything I wanted. "Anything I want, Dad?" French toast, eggs, pancakes, omelets, waffles. They had buffet after buffet of various breakfast foods, fruit, cereal, muffins and bagels, assorted juices and yogurt. I could not make up my mind. It was not until several years later when I stayed at another Embassy that I learned all of this stuff was free. Then after turning twenty-one and being allowed to order drinks quite a bit stronger than a kitty cocktail at the complimentary manager's reception, well there was just no turning back. Embassy Suites was solidified in my mind as the pillar of overnight accommodation.

I only stayed at a couple of more Embassy's before the year 2004 approached, when my hotel obsession really began to peak. Embassy Suites can be handsomely priced depending on location and date of stay. However, deals and low prices can always be found and booked frequently, as with all hotel chains, so I was always perusing the internet trying to find a cheap deal.

I started 2004 off with a bang in early January with a stay at the downtown Chicago Embassy Suites. Not the one by the lakefront, the other downtown location. In March, for spring break, it was northwest Arkansas as previously mentioned, and downtown St. Louis in the Landing, although now I believe that hotel is a Ritz. To celebrate a friend's twentieth birthday at the beginning of June, there was a three night stint at the St. Louis Airport Embassy. By the fall of 2004, with the help from a few other hotel stays, the points in my Hilton Honors account, of which I've been a member since 2003, were sizeable and I was bumped up to Silver status in the program. Boy, how I was rolling in the points and racking up the debt.

By the time it was nearing the end of 2004, I found myself living in a ridiculously over-priced one-bedroom shanty of a college apartment not far from campus. I was only taking classes two days a week and not foreseeing a graduation date anywhere in the near to distant future. I was traveling back home every other weekend to work at my twelve-hour shift factory job as I struggled, but managed, to make ends meet. All of this, and I still went out, partied, traveled, Pricelined, as if I assumed some distant relative was going to pass on and leave me sizeable monies, and this lifestyle would just easily be paid off. Yet there was one blessing. During the 2004-2005 school year, my dear, sweet angel of a sister lived with me, as she went to cosmetology school in the same town. Having her around and getting to spend a lot of time together during those nine months definitely brought us closer, and that time was truly cherished, even though I don't think she had any idea how tough I was having it, because I try hard not to show a dark side.

Christmas of 2004 was rapidly approaching as final exams were getting completed and I was looking forward to a break. As I checked my e-mail one early December day, I received an Embassy Suites E-Newsletter. Oh, undeniably, I was on their e-mail listserv. I was not getting laid or having any luck with women and it just dawned on me that, amongst other things, receiving a hotel's newsletter via e-mail while in college really does not emit strong sexuality, but does omit women from paying attention to you if that information is ever brought to light. Nevertheless, the newsletter always highlighted various Embassy's across the country and the respective deals they were having. As it were, the Embassy Suites in Deerfield, Illinois was offering a nightly rate of only $67 if booked online and was a weeknight stay. Factor in the money saved during the manager's reception and the amazing breakfast in the morning, I easily convinced myself that the room was practically free. I immediately booked a Tuesday night via credit card and was on my way to Deerfield a mere four days before Christmas.

I arrived at the Embassy early, checked in, and went up some stairs that were near the pool to the second floor and did not have to walk far to my room. I unlocked the door, walked in, set my bag down on the bed, and as routine would have it, asked myself, "Well, what now?" As usual, I decided to grab a bite to eat and take in a movie before the cocktail hour started at 5:30. The film *Closer* had recently come out and was playing at a nearby theater. I could not pass up a sexually charged film starring the equally gorgeous and talented Natalie Portman and Julia Roberts (whom, by the way, is a big Dave Matthews Band fan, which automatically ups her appeal).

I returned to the Embassy after the film, which I enjoyed, with a decent food base in my stomach for boozing. After a shower, I walked down to the reception area and ordered myself, not surprisingly, a screwdriver. Now, as I'm sure you can imagine, seeing as it was only days before Christmas, and a Tuesday evening at an Embassy in Deerfield, the hotel definitely was not rockin' with people. I simply sat alone at a table nearest the serving area and enjoyed my screwdrivers. Anticipating the scarcity of people at the hotel that evening, I had brought along some magazines from home to look through during the two-hour reception. The usual: Maxim, Stuff, FHM. Yet after a while it began turning into a vicious cycle. The more I flipped through the pages of these magazines and gazed upon the overwhelmingly gorgeous and scantily clad celebrities and hometown hotties, the quicker I drank and ordered drinks in an attempt to subdue the depression that was setting in as a result of knowing I will never be with women of such caliber. I can only assume women like that go for men who are attractive and successful. I want to meet those guys and just ask, "What is it like?" And it would make scum like me pleased to hear them respond with, "Eh, wasn't that great." But I think most men realize that simply would not be the case. It would be nothing less than heaven right here on earth, because there is nothing more sought after, more mysterious, or more beautiful than that of the female body.

The cocktail hour ended at 7:30 and I could tell I was on that slippery slope to another realm of existence. There was no way I could quit drinking at that point, not in the evening hours at an Embassy in Deerfield, IL. I mean, come on! I chucked my magazines in the trash as I found my way over to the hotel bar. There was no doubt the fine folks over at MasterCard would be footing the bill now, because the free drinks were already had. I planted myself at the end of the bar, only two stools down from a lovely couple also enjoying drinks, probably the only two other people staying at the hotel that night.

"What's your drink, sir?" the bartender asked.

"Screwdriver, please."

"Coming right up." As the bartender made my drink I took a look around behind me. There was literally no one else in sight. It felt surreal and almost dreamlike. I was sitting at a small hotel bar in a big open area that was relatively quiet, with only a few other people close to me. As the bartender handed me the drink, he asked, "Will this be charged to your room, sir?"

"That's right," I replied, "but keep the tab open." Feeling good, I looked over at the couple next to me. Both were smiling at each other, talking. Must be nice. I busted out my cell phone because I was at the point of drunkenness where texting felt to be a wise idea. I sent out a mass text to random friends.

SITTING ALONE AT EMBASSY SUITES BAR IN DEERFIELD WITH A HEAFTY BUZZ AND ZERO PROSPECTS. ENJOY YOUR HOLIDAY!

Over the next several minutes responses started to filter in.

WHERE'S DEERFIELD?

GOD YOU'RE SUCH A LOSER!

DOUCHEBAG

OH, MILES!

REALLY CRANKING UP THAT DEBT, AREN'T YA?

YOU DO REALIZE IT'S A TUESDAY?

I really do love my friends! After about twenty minutes of watching ESPN on low volume and another screwdriver later, I glanced back down to the couple at the bar, and happened to make eye contact with the woman. She smiled.

"So you're staying at the hotel tonight?" she asked.

"Yes indeed. You, too?"

"Yep. It's really quiet though."

"It sure is. I think we may be the only three people staying here tonight." The woman laughed. "My name is Miles, by the way." I'm much more confident with a solid drunk on.

"Hi, Miles. I'm Valerie, and this is my husband, Bill."

"Well, nice to meet you, Valerie. Bill." I flagged down the bartender. "Get Val and Bill here a drink on me." I hoped Valerie didn't mind that I immediately shortened her name due to pure laziness on my part.

"Awww, how sweet. Thank you, Miles," Valerie said. "So what brings you here?"

"Ummm, leisure I suppose. The hotel was running a great internet deal I just could not pass up."

"Huh. I see. So you're staying here strictly for the deal? No other reason really?"

"Hmmm ... I suppose not. A bit peculiar I guess when you think about it like that. I just love Embassy Suites, what can I say?"

"Honey," Bill said to his wife, "what was the name of that hotel we stayed at in the city a few months ago? Right near Navy Pier. It had that rooftop bar."

"Oh yeah, the W Hotel. Have you stayed there, Miles? The W on Lakeshore? It's really nice."

"No, but I'd like to. There are a ton of hotels I'd like to stay at. It's just the good people over at Visa and MasterCard won't give me high enough credit limits to stay at all of them!" I gave a slight chuckle. "I'm sorry. I think I'm in the low teens with these drinks," I said as I held up my half-empty glass.

"Just be careful with those credit cards, Miles," Valerie warned, "Bill and I pay cash for almost everything. I don't believe in credit cards. They are a black hole. Money issues are the number one reason why couples break up or get divorced, you know."

"Well I don't have to worry about that."

"Why?" she asked. "Don't you have a girlfriend or a wife? I find that hard to believe."

"Well believe it. I'm as single as they come. Probably nothing out on the horizon either I'm predicting."

"That's no attitude to have about it, Miles," Bill chimed in with, "confidence is half the battle. It's amazing where it will get you."

"That's right," Valerie responded, "you're a good looking young man. I would think it would be easy for you to get a date."

"Well it's easy for me to get restraining orders, I can tell you that. HA ... what?" I blankly stared at them during the moment of awkward silence after that remark. "Well that's nice of you to say. Another screwdriver, barkeep sir. But, Bill and Val, I do lack genuine confidence. I do not consider myself traditionally good looking or even non-traditionally good looking. I mean, look at my hair. What confident man would voluntarily do their hair like this? I also do not approach women well. I mean I got nothin' to say. I'm staying by myself in Deerfield on a Tuesday night for God's sake. This is not the kind of normal shit a guy my age should be doing, and it's not something that constitutes as a legitimate conversation starter. 'Hi, my name is Miles and I frequently stay alone in random hotels.'"

"That one's on us," Bill said to the bartender as he placed in front of me what would ultimately be my last drink. "Miles, you have to look at what is genuinely good inside yourself and apply those attributes when speaking to women. There's nothing wrong with staying alone in hotels, everyone needs to get away sometimes. Granted, it's probably not a subject to be broached on a first date, but ultimately you just have to be yourself, my friend."

"Is there not anyone you're interested in, Miles?" Valerie asked.

"Oh jeez. I don't know." I sighed. "Ya know, I occasionally think about this one girl I met. But it could never go anywhere."

"Well why not?" Bill asked.

"Because she's hundreds of miles and an entire state away living in Arkansas. I met her back in March when I was down in Bentonville on spring break taking a tour of the very first Wal-Mart. Also, Bill, not a story that really screams 'dateable'."

"I have heard it's pretty down there," Valerie randomly stated.

"Yeah, it's nice. But you two are right. I *was* myself when we spoke to each other. We talked for over two hours at an Embassy Suites, much like we're doing now, and it was amazing. And man was she gorgeous. This auburn hair that could light up a room. But I try not to think about it too much because I'll never see her again."

I was getting drunker and could feel my eyelids starting to get heavy. It was just a matter of time before I said something completely inappropriate.

"You never know, Miles. If two people are meant to be together, somehow their lives will lead them in a direction to where their paths will ultimately cross. Just like you and this girl. You'll see."

"No. No I won't see, Valerie! And do you want to know why I won't see? You really want to know the true reason I'm so unsuccessful with women? Because I've never been with one."

"Excuse me?" Valerie asked, perplexed.

"You heard correctly. I've never had sex. I'm a virgin. A twenty-two year old freakin' virgin. I went through high school. I'm in my fourth year of college. And nothin'! I'm constantly surrounded by people having a great time, going out, hooking up, and I'm just the creep in the corner at the party, having no fun, no sex." I looked down, ran my fingers through my hair, and took a deep breath. I stood up from my barstool. "I'm sorry. I need to go. I've had too much to drink. I should not be speaking about things like this."

"Miles," Valerie said, "look, don't go."

"No, I've embarrassed myself ... yet again. You two were great."

"Come on, just listen real quick, Miles. I'm going to tell you something only because I know, well Bill and I know, what you're going through. Please stay." I turned my entire body around to face them, one hand holding my drink and the other clutching the back of a barstool as I listened to Valerie. "Bill and I had never been with anyone when we met each other. God's honest truth. Our paths crossed at a young age, we fell in love, and have been happily married for almost twenty years. We're the only people each other have been with and we could not be happier. Sure, maybe we're the exception to some bogus rule, but sex does not define people, Miles. It is not everything. It's just ... an added bonus. Some people mull through life having all the random sex anyone could want, but they are never truly happy. Don't be upset that you're a virgin, it's not a bad thing. You will eventually find what you're looking for. And when you do find that special person who will ultimately be your first, you'll realize you waited for a reason. And sure, being with them for the first time will be great, but knowing in your heart that you waited and did it right, well, that's a noble thing. Possibly the best of things."

After Valerie was finished speaking, I stared at her and Bill for a moment as tears had faintly welled up in my eyes. "I hope you're right, Valerie and Bill. Thanks for the drink."

I let go of the stool and left the bar, and eventually managed to stumble back to my room. I stood at the edge of my bed. I was tired and upset but I knew there was no way I could sleep. I was also drunk and pissed off and Valerie's words kept flowing in and out of my mind. I hastily grabbed my swimming trunks from my bag and changed into them, which proved to be a chore. I left my room and wobbly made it down to the pool. I knew a swim would sober me up a bit, so I immediately headed to the hot tub, fully realizing a sulk would further my inebriated state.

There was not a single other soul in the pool area as I stood above the hot tub looking down at the water, swaying. I went and turned the jets on, which reminded me of that flawless mother from the hot tub at the Hilton in Oakbrook Terrace months earlier. The memory of her combined with how I was already feeling prompted a dive into further depression and self-pity. And, since there was no one in sight and I was intoxicated, I busted out of my suit and slid into that hot tub stark naked. What did I care?

I boiled in that hot tub as my head sweated and swayed and my blood thinned. Lord how I was gonna have a headache in the morning. I sat in that hot tub with my eyes half-closed as the bubbles raced around my disgusting naked body. The negative thoughts just poured into my head.

What have I become? How did I end up like this? God I'm so alone. Just so alone.

I struggled to keep my eyes open.

I had obviously fallen asleep at some point because I awoke to the sound of a voice, my head resting back on the floor looking up at the lights. The jets had shut off.

"Sir, the pool area is closing. Sir?"

I slowly lifted my head up and looked around, confused.

"Sir, you're going to have to leave. The pool area is closing."

As my eyes came into focus I noticed the night manager standing in the doorway on the other side of the room. "Whatchoo say?"

"I said the pool area is closing. You need to get out of the hot tub."

"Jus gimmie ... a sec." Oh was I hammered. I heaved my body to the left and grabbed onto the hot tub railing. I started to walk up the stairs, my back to the manager.

"Oh my God!" I heard the night manager yell. "Oh my God! Sir? What are you doing? Get your suit on and get out!"

I stumbled over to my suit.

"What of it?" I yelled back. I was angry and drunk, and cold.

"Just put your suit on and get out of this room!"

I struggled getting one leg into my suit at a time, but I finally accomplished it, albeit they were on backwards. I slowly staggered toward the manager. "There's a problems, sir?" I asked begrudgingly.

"Sir, you cannot be nude in or around the pool area. That violates a number of laws and policies."

"I jus ... wanna go for a dip. I go back to my room."

"Sir, you're clearly drunk and you could have very easily drowned. I'm in half a mind to call the police. Just go back to your room and sleep it off before I change my mind."

"I'm silver Honors status, sir!" I stated, as if being in the second tier of the Hilton Honors program justified being passed out naked and drunk in a hotel hot tub.

"I'm not going to tell you again. Get back to your room! And I do not want to see you at this hotel again for a very long time."

"Aye, aye, sir."

I left the pool area and meandered my drunken self back to my room. The night manager watched me the entire time until he heard my door click shut. Once I got into my room I whipped off my suit again and barely made it to the bed. It was nearing the end of 2004 and I was nowhere closer to accomplishing anything with school, a girl, financially, just nothing. And it all sunk in as I bottomed out. I needed desperately for the next year to bring some sort of change. I blacked out on that king size bed for the next ten hours, but not before thinking and mumbling to myself, "You are nothing. Absolutely nothing."

One Year Later...

The Fourteenth Chapter

Thoughts of a Nautical Nature

O ne year later. Pretty clichéd and overused, yes? We see it all of the time in movies. *One year later. Six weeks later. Four minutes later.* I suppose as an audience we are to assume relatively nothing happened over that period of time and everything stayed basically the same, and if something significant did happen, are we to assume it simply was not relevant enough to the particular story being told? Well my *one year later* usage falls under the first assumption.

From December 2004 to December 2005 almost literally nothing happened. Nothing changed. I was still living in my one-bedroom shit-hole apartment outside of campus, my sister had moved out, and my college roommate from two years prior had moved in to help ease my financial burdens, and sacrificed an actual bed for a futon in my living room. He was pursuing his Master's degree at the time as he had followed the collegiate timeline appropriately, whereas I was in the middle of the multi-year Bachelor program with a graduation date expected to coincide with my becoming an AARP member.

I found myself in as deep of debt, excluding college loans, as I ever had. I attended seven Dave Matthews Band concerts during this span. Three of them being at the Gorge Amphitheater out in Washington State. To boot, I had flown into Seattle-Tacoma Airport to attend those shows straight from Las Vegas where I had just spent three nights at the Bellagio, a far cry from the garbage Las Vegas motel I had stayed at three years prior. Despite the fact it was the best week of my entire life, and having the good fortune of the Bellagio room being paid for by a friend's uncle, the week overall was just a financial train wreck. The term 'fiscally irresponsible' had become an understatement. But, you know, we only live once, so we're told. I feel by that point I had to be considered one of Visa and MasterCard's most valued members because the interest charges were just pouring in.

And there was one more thing. What was it? Oh yes. Still not getting laid! Virginity spewed from my veins and that V-card was securely fastened to my balls. A point came in which I was seriously considering punching holes in the upper two corners of a 4x6 index card, hanging the card around my neck with a noticeably bright piece of yarn just long enough to where the card covered my genital region, and have written on the card with a black Sharpie the words **NOT IN USE**. I could walk around campus that way, my virginity yarn card swinging in the breeze, since that was the message I was so prominently conveying.

No degree. No money. No sex. I was twenty-three years old and basically living the same life as a pre-pubescent child. Only now I had bills. But in spite of this, there were many times where I would think to myself about how so many other people were in the same unstable boat I was. Not only that, but how many people's boats must be sinking, and on those sinking boats are people with families to support, single parents, unemployed people, folks who are losing their home, hungry people, the terminally ill. And people try so hard to turn things around, to become better, but ultimately the same end is in sight. It would be just as useful as rearranging the chairs on the Titanic.

It's so miserably sad.

But then there was me. I managed to get through every day and go to sleep every night in a warm bed with my ship somehow remaining afloat. There was only myself and I was the only one who had to live with the choices I made. I had no children, no dependents. I had a job and an apartment. A friend who was generous enough to sleep in my living room and pay half of the bills. Amazing family and friends. Great teachers. I had my health. It came down to looking at what I had versus the choices I was making. I chose to travel and live beyond my means via credit. I chose to swipe those cards on unnecessary things at unnecessary times. I chose to take the minimal number of credit hours only two days a week per semester, and then refused to take summer courses. I chose not to find a second job to help ease the burden. I chose to have such high standards with women that all it did was get me none at all. It simply comes down to the choices we make. But everything that was good in my life seemed to balance out the bad. I woke up every morning with my boat still floating, but still waiting for a change. And as the man says,

"Everyday things change, but basically they stay the same." [1]

Then one day I received an e-mail.

I was sitting at my computer in the lone bedroom of my apartment in early December of 2005 when I noticed what appeared to be a personal e-mail from an address I did not recognize, with a subject line that read "Remember?" I opened the e-mail with stout curiosity.

> Miles,
>
> I hope this is still your address. You may not remember, but you and I once chatted over drinks. If you'd like to chat again, please call me. Did you ever get that book written? Hope to hear from you.
> R.

A phone number was also left, but I really could not think of who it may be, and the vagueness of the message concerned me a bit. No name was given, only what I assumed was an initial. The location where the supposed drinks and chat had taken place was not revealed. The e-mail's author did, however, bring up the hopeless book I was always telling people I wanted to write, and I do enjoy pretending I'm a writer when I meet people. I speak to random people all of the time when I'm drinking that I fail to ever see again. The mysteriousness of the e-mail overwhelmed me, and since I basically had nothing else significant in my life, the e-mail and prospect of calling this person was all I thought about.

A few days had passed when I came to the conclusion that not too much harm could be done by giving the number a call. What's the worst that could happen? If the person turned out to be some kind of whack job lunatic, all I would have needed to do was change my e-mail address. I went to Wal-Mart and bought a sixty minute phone card, among other things, because one can never leave Wal-Mart with only what was intended to be bought. My reasoning for the phone card was such that I presumed this person had caller ID, and my hope was that the phone card would prevent my actual number from showing up. So that evening, while my living room futon roommate was at class, I sat on the edge of my bed, followed the calling card instructions, and dialed the number. It rang once. Twice. Thr ...

"Hello?" a woman's voice answered.

---

1 Dave Matthews, *Seek Up*

"Um, yes. Hello. Um, my name is Miles, and I received an e-mail the other day with this ... "

"Oh my God!!" the woman bellowed, cutting me off. "I wasn't sure if you'd call or not. Oh my God! Do you know who this is?"

"Well the e-mail didn't say much. Pretty vague actually. That's probably why it took me a few days to call. I assume you're 'R' though."

"Yes, that's totally me."

I wanted to ask, "Oh *ARE* you?" But I figured such a lame attempt at humor that early in the conversation would do neither of us any good. Instead I asked, "Is there more after the R?"

"Miles, it's Raven. Raven from Arkansas. Do you remember?"

About a thousand images poured into my head almost immediately, the first being that flowing auburn-red hair, which stuck with me for a moment until every other image started to jumble up. Embassy Suites. Screwdriver drinks. Talking to a man in the bathroom. A sundress. Kelly and Ashley jumping on the bed. Sitting alone at a table. Paying a dollar for drinks. Crossed legs. Hotel stationary. It seemed all of the images from that night came and went in about four seconds. I didn't want to be too lagged in my response.

"Raven? Oh, wow! I never thought I'd hear that name again. This is so crazy. I mean ... how are you?"

"Good. I'm good. Still going to school. Going to be graduating next May though, finally! It seems like it will never get here. How are things with you?"

"Me? Oh I'm fine. Getting by. Also still in school, but without a definite graduation date quite yet. You know, I like to keep people guessing."

She laughed. "Well the important thing is you're sticking with it. The commitment is what it's all about. It doesn't matter how long it takes you, just as long as you get it done. My gosh, I still can't believe you called!"

"You?" I asked. "I'm, like, still in total shock. The fact I'm even talking to you again is such a great surprise. I have to ask, though, why did you e-mail me and not just call?"

"Well, I'll tell you, I was going through and organizing my desk and storage bins and things, and I came across a piece of paper in one of my old Caboodles that had 'Embassy Suites' printed on top, and written below was all your info."

She actually kept the paper. I couldn't believe it. "That's incredible! I can't believe you kept that."

"Yeah. It took me a few to remember who 'Miles' was, but once it came to me, I remembered what a nice time we had, so I dialed the phone number on the piece of paper a few times, but this girl kept answering and telling me she had no idea who you were, and told me to quit calling. I thought maybe it was your girlfriend and she got upset because another girl was calling you. That's when I decided it would probably be safer to just send the e-mail."

"Well, believe me, Raven, if I actually *had* a girlfriend she would still probably tell people she had no idea who I was. But I remember now. I switched cell phone providers a few months after the Arkansas trip and my number changed, so who knows who you were talking to."

"Well I called like three times. The final time the girl just hung up, she didn't even say a word. But the nice thing is we're talking now. So, I want to hear all about your book."

I sighed. "Yeah, I'd like to hear about it too! It's still a total pipe dream. I don't have the slightest idea where to begin or even what to write about. I'm a good number of semesters into the English and Writing program up here and I still can't come up with an original idea that I can run with."

"Well it's totally hard to come up with something completely original anymore, at least something that's quality. I'm sorry you're having such a hard time, Miles. Maybe you could collaborate with a classmate or something."

"Maybe. But that's the thing. I'll read stories my classmates have written and am completely blown away. Some of them are so talented it makes me question whether I should even put forth the effort. I don't know. I've been telling people recently that I'm working on a book, but not doing any actual writing. It's all imaginary, and I'm sure people will forget I ever said anything about it. Ah well, enough about that. Are you still studying ... interior design was it?"

"Yup, still plugging away. I can't believe you remember that. I was just glad I found something I actually wanted to stick with. I really do enjoy it though. I hope I'm able to find work right after I graduate. My lease is up at the end of May so I'm going to start job hunting and take something wherever I can get it."

"My lease is up then, too. I'm anxious to get out of this one-bedroom insufficient apartment."

"Hey now, I have a one-bedroom and I love it. Very cozy. It's not like I need more room for a boyfriend or anything."

I kind of figured Raven was single or else she probably would not have called. I liked the fact she was single, even though I was miffed by it. I'm not exactly sure why I even enjoyed that fact, it's not as if I was ever going to see her.

"You're telling me there aren't guys lined up outside your door waiting to take you out?"

"Oh, now come on, Miles. I've seen a few guys here and there, but nothing serious. I really need to focus on school. I'm not sure if you remember me telling you, but I've been paying for college on my own, so graduating is doubly important."

I did remember. "Well I think it's great you're so passionate. I'm very happy for you. A little jealous maybe, but definitely happy."

Raven giggled. "So, Miles, how did the rest of your spring break trip end up turning out last year?"

Before I knew it, a voice came on the phone telling me I only had two minutes left on my card. That hour spent talking to Raven flew by. It was as if she and I had spoken every week for the past year and a half, and after our conversation was over, I wished we had.

The Fifteenth Chapter

An Amateur Proposition

Conversations with Raven continued as such for a while. I even changed my cell phone plan so my free nights and weekends started at 7:00. We would talk two or three times a week. It was doing me good to have something to look forward to. I mean, don't get me wrong, it's not like going back to an inadequate apartment after taking writing classes surrounded by people with talent and imagination only to discover my roommate passed out on a futon in my living room was not thrilling for me. It was. But just above that was the thought of meaningful conversation with a classy, genuinely kind person a few nights a week whose laugh never failed to bring a smile to my face.

The more we spoke, the more comfortable she and I felt with what we would tell each other. I never had too much to say that was on the deeply serious side. There are always bumps along the way, but aside from my own selfishly created personal affairs, I have gratefully lived a fairly painless and drama-free life. I would just sit back and listen to Raven talk. After a while it became apparent to me that perhaps she simply wanted, or needed, someone to not only talk with, but more importantly to listen.

As long as I kept on listening, the further Raven delved into what she revealed about herself. She did not hold much back. As it turned out, she had done some modeling work to help pay for college. Not only modeling, but some nude modeling as well. When she told me about this, I don't think I need to say I was more than curious to see those pictures. Yet, I was a gentleman and did not ask to see them or even cut a joke about her sending them to me. But as luck would have it, and her being the open and carefree person she was, she sent me the pictures voluntarily, only after I made sure she was comfortable doing so. The classiness and tastefulness in which the pictures were taken roused my interest in Raven even further. They were not nude pictures taken simply for the fact to be naked, I could tell the photographer took his or her time, and that Raven appeared so natural and comfortable I would have thought it was a common thing, but I guess the nude sessions were just a one-time deal.

Furthermore, she went into some detail about the rocky relationship she had with her step-father. The first thing she said about him is that he was not a bad man, but lacked the heart of a good man. Raven explained to me that about a year after her parents divorced, she was out shopping with her mother. Raven was browsing along as her mother was paying for clothes, when apparently an older man approached and started chatting with Raven and subtly hitting on her. Raven was not quite twenty years old at the time. She tried to dismiss and ignore the man, but he was persistent. A few minutes passed before the man finally backed off. Raven went about her shopping while waiting for her mother to return. After Raven asked her mother what took so long, her mother explained how she had just met this gentleman at the check-out counter and that he had asked her to lunch, to which she obliged. As it were, the gentleman Raven's mother was so smitten with was the same man who had hit on her nineteen year old daughter not ten minutes prior. They were married a year later. Raven does not have much to do with him.

It was around this same time, after her mother had remarried, Raven had been accepted to the University of Arkansas in Fayetteville, not far from Bentonville. Raven was ecstatic upon being accepted, but was at a loss on how she was going to pay. She could not turn to the government for help because both of her parents, despite being divorced, each had household incomes which were too high to qualify for financial assistance, and her parents were only willing to help her out to a certain point.

Raven proceeded to tell me she had met some people while she was modeling who had consistently told her of a way she could make a significant amount of money, but she always rejected their suggestions. That was until she had been accepted to college but had no way of paying for it. She claimed to be without a choice. Raven continued on to tell me that after she was accepted to college, she contacted these people, who made her an offer. So it became, that when she was nineteen years old, in the summer before her first semester began, she accepted an offer to go to Oklahoma to make a film. My curiosity brewed. I thought maybe it was an educational video of sorts, perhaps a safety video. Come to learn, there was nothing educational or safe about it. Raven went on to tell me she not only went to Oklahoma, but willingly starred in a film of the pornographic persuasion.

After she told me this, I consciously made the effort not to be silent long, because the longer I was quiet, the more she would think I was judging her, which I wasn't.

"How do you feel about it now, Raven," I asked, "now that a few years have passed?"

"Miles, don't you remember? I told you on that couch at the Embassy that getting the money together for college was extremely daunting, but you got to do what you got to do. That's all there is to it. Sometimes when we're walking down our path of life, we come to a crossroad, and we have to decide which direction to take, Miles. We *have* to choose."

"Yes, and I appreciate that, Raven. But how do you feel about it *now*?"

"I feel the same about it now as I did when I was making the damn thing. I felt nothing. I could not allow myself to feel. It was my choice, and I live with it. Everyday. But between the money I made modeling and the money from the video, plus the little my parents gave me, in addition to working part-time, I am paying for college, and in May I am going to graduate. And for that, I'm grateful. Sometimes you have to go to some dark places, Miles, to really see the light."

She felt nothing, and so did I. I agreed with what she said. "Well I admire you for that, Raven. I surely do." I was happy I was able to tell her that too, because I had made the mistake a few years earlier of failing to tell Requisite the exotic dancer what I admired about her. Sometimes that's all people need to hear. I continued, "bottom line though, Raven, is now I've got to figure out how to get my hands on a copy of this thing!"

Raven laughed. "Oh, Miles. Well good luck! I don't think it had very high distribution." Moments of silence passed. I thought perhaps Raven felt she had told me too much, and was starting to feel embarrassed and did not want to speak anymore. But I was wrong. "You know, Miles, we've been talking quite regularly for well over a month now. We've definitely become close and I have really enjoyed it. I feel a comfort when I talk to you and tell you intimate things that I've never really felt with anyone else. Do you feel it?"

"What I know, is that I think about you all the time, and I have dreams where you're there, and I know I don't want to wake up. So yeah ... I feel it."

"Miles...," she paused. "Miles, I think you should come down here again. I want you to come down."

To be honest, I was more shocked by this proposition then when she admitted she was an amateur porn artist.

"I'm sorry, Raven. You want me to go back down? Back down to Arkansas?"

"Don't you think it would be fun? You could come down for a weekend or something. I just want to see you again, Miles. You have become a nice part of my life over the past six weeks. Even if it's just for one night, I don't care. You would not regret it. I promise."

I really didn't know what to think. It was obvious she did not remember too well my lack of features or physique, or the proposal would not have been presented in the first place. Nor her initial e-mail for that matter. After she asked me, though, a small part of me wanted to hop in my car that night and begin the trek down there. However, a larger part of me began questioning the stability of the woman. I found it a tad odd that a woman I've only been speaking on the phone with for a little over a month, whom I'd met only one time, and shared innocent casual conversation and drink with, almost two years earlier, wanted me to travel over five-hundred miles to spend time together. This was something I would have to deeply ponder.

I eventually came to the conclusion that we did not know each other near well enough to even contemplate me traveling down to meet in person again. Sure, we had shared intimate details from our lives with each other, well mainly her, and there was a definite connection of sorts, but doing something like this is a huge risk and massive undertaking. The money aspect alone was reason enough not to go. I was already in significant financial dire straits, and then to tackle something like that? Moronic. I could only imagine what my financial planner and life coach would have said if I were not so stubborn to actually have either one of the two.

But the underlying aspect to all of this was the almost guaranteed prospect of sex. She knew it. I knew it—despite my overwhelmingly poor familiarity with the physical act itself.

Once that notion was cemented in my virginal thoughts, just the idea of possible sex, I found myself contemplating the trip more and more. I would think about it during class. During work. I had trouble falling asleep at night. I would lie in my bed staring up at the ceiling, the thought of being with her made my heart race, and I would lie there alone, thinking how I never have a woman lying next to me. How I go to bed every night alone, and wake up on mornings just the same. Completely alone. No one to lie there and talk with. To hold. To touch. To kiss. To laugh with under the covers. Never. I was thankful for all of the great things in my life. But the physical connection made between two people making love, the romance of it all, had eluded me.

Eventually I decided I needed an outside perspective and opinion on the entire matter. What I really needed was for someone to talk me completely out of the notion of returning to Arkansas, or for someone to give me a legitimate reason why I *should* go. I chose to consult the man who was pursuing his Master's degree by day, and sleeping on a futon in my living room at night. My old roommate, O'Brien. I never call him by his first name.

I mixed O'Brien and myself some screwdrivers one evening in mid-January of 2006 and sat him down for a chat. I told him that despite my better judgment and lack of options, I needed his input on a matter of which was way beyond our maturity level.

I explained to O'Brien the details of that evening with Raven at the Embassy Suites in 2004. About why I had always been tight-lipped regarding the venture and made conscious efforts to never tell anyone about Raven and mine's little encounter, mainly for the sake of not coming off as desperate by going around telling people what a great time I had for a few hours with this girl whom I'd met only once that lived over five-hundred miles away. These random encounters happen everywhere to people all of the time, and they remain just that, simple encounters. Also, if I did decide to take this little venture, someone really should be informed of my whereabouts. I mean, the death factor on this trip was considerably higher than what I felt comfortable with. All things considered, Raven and I really did not truly *know* each other that well. She could very easily turn out to be a complete psychotic who ends up drugging my drinks and proceeds to castrate me with an old protractor she used in high school geometry class, only to dump my body in some remote Arkansas field and leave me for dead.

O'Brien assured me something like that happening was highly unlikely. I went on to tell him about the rocky life she had led those past few years. The circumstances surrounding her step-father, her parents not helping out much with her tuition, etc. And by "etc" I mean I told O'Brien that Raven claimed to have starred in a hardcore film when she was nineteen to gain college funds. He was surprised I was able to keep all of this to myself for so long, but even more shocked by the fact this girl wanted to see me again.

"This has 'one night stand' written all over it, buddy," O'Brien asserted. "But am I safe in assuming she probably does not remember too much about you?"

"I've considered that assumption, and I'm leaning toward the negative," I responded.

"Well if you do decide to do this you would have to stay at a hotel, because seeing as you may think this chick is unstable, and the idea of her wanting to have sex with you basically assures us that she is, you want to try to stay in public at all times, and not stay over at her place, because who knows what type of Buffalo Bill shit she's capable of. I mean we could be talking *The Silence of the Virgin* here, Miles. Am I right? And only book a hotel room for one night, and if things go well, then you can consider staying longer."

"Okay. So you mean, like, stay at the Embassy again?" I asked.

"Yes, fine, the Embassy, if that helps you. Your obsession with that hotel chain is beyond ordinary." O'Brien finished his drink and set his glass on the table. He sat up, placed his elbows on his knees, put his hands together, and pointed towards me. "Alright, Miles, here's what I think. We've already established that it's safe to assume this chick wants you. And keeping in mind your history with women, or lack thereof, you're not getting any younger here. The fact you've gone through this much college without getting laid still baffles me, but not too many guys can say they lost their V-card to a porn star. On the other hand, it would be much cheaper, and a little safer, to simply go out and find some random, willing girl right here on campus to bring back to this dump and humiliate yourself with. But having said that, you've gone this long without, so waiting longer really is not an issue for you. So the question is not really a matter of when, but whom? The ball's in your court, so to speak. Patience has proven not to be an issue for you. What has proven to be an issue is your lack of confidence and obvious too high of standards. Look, remember our In-n-Out Burger Vegas trip back in '02? How we planted the idea in our heads to go and then just got up and did it? We still talk about it to this day. It's all about the story, Miles. It always has been, and always will be. And this could end up being the greatest story you will ever tell. I say go for it man."

I let out a deep breath and thanked O'Brien for his honesty and shook his hand. He had fulfilled the duties of a roommate admirably, and those of a friend. I laid awake that night in bed, staring at the ceiling as usual, mulling over everything. However that night, after considering everything I possibly could personally, financially, sexually, morally, I came to a conclusion, and fell into the deepest sleep I'd had in a while. What I was basically foreseeing on the horizon was the possibility of guilt-free sex with a potential adult film star at an Embassy Suites hotel just minutes from the birthplace of Wal-Mart. How could any hotel loving, Wal-Mart obsessed, V-card carrying guy say no to this?

The next morning I awoke and knew what I had to do. I called her up. She answered.

"Raven," I said. "I'm in."

The Voice of Reason: What Lies Therein

"So, Miles, I see you went crying and complaining about me to your bartender friend Kyle a few chapters back. Can't take the heat, huh? Well, if you want to have a genuine conversation, then let's have one. You are, after all, nearing the end of this atrocity and I fail to see how anything more I say is going to stop you now. You know who you remind me of? The character of Miles from the novel and film *Sideways*. You share the same name, you're both struggling writers, you're drunks, have problems with the ladies. The only difference is that you don't like wine and he occasionally gets laid."

"Oh, yes, I am Miles from *Sideways*. And who are you ... my best friend Jack? What I am attempting to do here is give you an opportunity to say what you feel you need to say instead of just dismissing you. I'm allowing you an outlet here so maybe you won't feel as much of a need to interrupt me between chapters and disturb the flow of the book."

"See, that's the sort of thing I've been hammering you about. What 'flow' are you referring to? This book is all over the place. Too many dates, various locations, you introduce random characters whom have hardly any description and their relevance to your story not made all that clear. There are a few chapters that are completely futile and do not serve the main story at all. By the way, what exactly is the main story anyway? I believe I recall you saying back in the twelfth chapter, 'It's about some chick and some dude.' How inherently juvenile."

"I'm just going to come out and say that for a first attempt at writing something significant and meaningful, I am quite pleased with how it has turned out. I talked about writing a book for God knows how long, so to have something actually come to fruition is exciting for me. It has definitely turned into the book I set out to write."

"Awww ... that's cute, Miles. It's *exciting* for you! Well this may be the book you set out to write, but it's not the book anyone will set out to read. I've seen more intelligent writing in men's bathroom stalls. Just look back, the book is totally short! It strongly reiterates your complete lack of detail. I don't understand why you keep referring to it as a book or novel, when it clearly reads 'novella' on the cover."

"Quantity and length really does not concern me. It's quality."

"Applying the same philosophy to this book as you do to acts in the bedroom, are you? Quality over quantity and length. *Oh, don't worry sweetheart, this will only take a minute. But that minute will be mind blowing! What's your name again hun?* The standards you set for yourself regarding this book, Miles, are unprecedentedly low, and your writing very much reflects that. I touched on this before. You think the actual writing is the hard part? Have you even done any research on what to do after it's written? Do you even know the first step in trying to get published?"

"No, honestly, I have not done much research regarding publishing. I want to concentrate on the writing first and worry about the logistics of it later. I am well aware that getting published is no cake walk."

"Yes, procrastinate. That's done wonders for you so far. Did you not procrastinate for an entire decade to try to write something substantial? Are you aware of literary agents? Don't tell me you believe publishing this thing would be as simple as sending it to a publishing house? You will most certainly need an agent considering your massive ignorance regarding the world of publishing. In other words, you're going to need to find an agent who actually enjoys reading your garbage and hope that he or she can find an even more willing publisher to distribute your writing to a public that will not enjoy it at all. Plus, think of all the money you'll spend at Kinkos making copies, packaging and posting for mailing to agents, self-addressed stamped envelopes to provide them so they can send you rejection letters. Even self-publishing, which in your case is probably a more realistic route, is still very expensive. When and how do you think you'll attain this money? You spoke about your mounting debt and fledgling fiscal responsibility. If you could have only predicted that swiping those credit cards one-thousand too many ridiculous times would result in possibly keeping you from publishing the book you would eventually write, perhaps you would have spent less time at Wal-Mart, or traveling, or on Priceline, or out getting shit-faced, and spent more time with pen to paper!"

"What are you getting at?"

"WHAT AM I GETTING AT?? What I'm getting at is you could be living comfortably right now if you had not been such a monetary incompetent! Perhaps your next piece of writing could be a study of credit cards and the damaging effects they can cause, providing the stress caused by trying to get this piece of trash published doesn't send you to an early grave first. And speaking of the money concerns, what did you do near the end of 2006? Huh? You went out and purchased a brand new car. Just the thing a fresh college grad needs who is about to start taking on more than twenty grand in student loans. You're not part of any current economic solution, Miles, you're very much part of the problem! And you didn't even buy a manly vehicle either. A chick magnet. A Ford Mustang or a big new heavy duty truck. Nope. What you financed at a ridiculously high interest rate was a 2006 four-cylinder Kia Spectra. Most guys at that age are buying vehicles with balls, vehicles that scream multiple orgasms. Your vehicle, as it is, screams erectile dysfunction. That leaf blower of yours with beach ball tires should have **PLAYSKOOL** painted on the bumper and the word **CIALIS** on the license plate. What a blatantly awful decision that was. But I think we've come to expect that from you."

"God bless it, now you're just reaching. It's not enough you rip apart my book, but now you have to veer off onto my vehicle and finances? Just spew out your points regarding the book so you and I can be done with each other!"

"Korean manufactured vehicles a touchy subject with you, Miles? I thought this was an opportunity for me to voice my opinions, no? I simply keep failing to understand what you're trying to accomplish here and your refusal to truly consider the things I have been telling you throughout. For instance, the random stories you tell are not thoroughly laid out so the reader cannot fully grasp the meaning or significance behind them. This female character, Raven, became a large part of this book, but I for one have a difficult time picturing her in my head because you do not appropriately describe her, nor yourself for that matter. For all I know, you're both just floating heads with blank faces on non-existent bodies. Only she has auburn-red hair. And the dialogue between you too ... forget it. It's completely boring and uninspired. I guarantee I could have a more intriguing conversation with an infant! The incoherent verbiage that spews out of that garbage disposal mouth of yours is embarrassing. Are you really that dull to talk with? My God! I get more stimulated listening to Canadian Parliament."

"That's seriously how you picture Raven and I? As floating heads? She is definitely no Sarah plain and tall, I'll tell you that!"

"Well too bad you're a Miles lame and impotent. So Sarah wins!"

"And all I am hoping is that maybe a few people will get a chuckle reading some of the stories in here. If something makes me laugh you can almost guarantee it will make someone else laugh as well."

"Talk about reaching. And is this 'someone' being the one and only person to buy this book?"

"Also, has it ever occurred to you that the readers do not care about all of your opinions? All you really seem to be doing is providing hasty generalizations. Do you even know what constitutes *good* writing?"

"Do you, Miles? And hasty generalizations? Let me explain this to you like the English major you claim to be. You are assuming that there are not any agreed upon principles applicable to a given piece of writing. For instance, bad grammar is generally understood as a matter not of opinion, but of adherence to specific rules. And your piece of writing here is riddled with grammatical errors, among other things, sentence fragments, comma splices, run-ons, incomplete sentences, punctuality errors, usage of quotation marks and italics, too many words ending with –*ly*, etc. You use these (...) way too often. And, by the way, the fact you are pointing out your own mistakes does not merit the excuse to just let them go uncorrected. What I've been trying to do all along is not give you just harsh critique, Miles, but true arbitrary assessment, of which I have no idea why. All you've got is a dirty mind and a filthy mouth, and your writing reflects as such. Nothing but a book of smut."

"Alright, yes, I agree, the grammar may not be perfect, and I am certainly not a model reflection of the fine English and Writing departments of my alma mater. But no, I am certainly not above referencing my own work, nor bringing myself into my writing. What you fail to see is that what you find to be complete trash, someone else may find to be entertaining. Not all opinions are equal. They are subjective. I do not feel things need to be changed. I am writing what I want to write and how I want to write it. Therein lies the beauty of writing, which is something you are failing to recognize."

"Am I? Or are you just too ignorant to comprehend anything, Miles? You're glossing over your own words and not truly reading between your poorly written lines. All you need to do is look back over what you've written.

Did you seriously at one point think of your life in terms of boating? As being on a ship? Miles, your ship has long since capsized and sunken into the deep depths of an empty ocean from which you may never rise. What kind of a freakin' outlook is that? And also, you mentioned early on about not writing to a specific audience or caring who reads your work. I strongly suggest reconsidering this. I'm going to retract the statement I made when you and I first spoke and tell you that family members are *not* the only people who are going to be reading this. Allow me to magnify the main core of people you need to be concerned about. Your parents, grandparents, aunts and uncles, cousins, extended family, parents and families of your friends. Co-workers, your boss, old teachers, townsfolk and elders of your community that may not be familiar with you, but hey, someone from their town wrote a book, so why not take a look-see? They proceed to open the cover and read the first few pages which speak solely of strippers and your hatred of community colleges. You go on to discuss unhealthily serious obsessions with Wal-Mart and hotels and travel and William Shatner endorsed websites. It is no mystery you were never getting laid, as those are not attributes a typical twenty-something should posses or fixate over. You bring up your ignorance of the term 'sexual chocolate' which cements three words I have about you from my own personal repertoire: YOU. ARE. WHITE. Continuing on, you devote an entire chapter to a word that a good number of folks refuse to say nor want to read. Does that kind of language resonate from your vocabulary frequently? Then the kicker, you pass out naked in a hotel hot tub and then verbally harass the night manager as if kicking you out was infringing on your rights as a guest! Seriously? You then proceed into great detail about your blossoming non-existent sex life as casually as if it were proper Sunday dinner conversation. And the cherry on top is that you delve into remembering an encounter with a woman who is dangerously unpredictable and whom convinces you she was at one time an employee of the adult film industry. You easily believe this about her and as if there is nothing to lose, you dive deeper into debt by deciding to go pay her a visit in northwest Arkansas. Are all of these stories and attributes and qualities about yourself truly something you are comfortable sharing with the aforementioned groups of people? Or any other human being for that matter? You should be seriously worried about how certain people are going to react to your writing! I guarantee you'll get a lot of, 'Did that actually happen? Is that true? Do you realize how embarrassed

I am that I know you? I didn't know you were really like this.' You're being very selfish with this and not considering how this may affect others around you. I mean, where do you find the entitlement to call yourself a writer, Miles? If you were truly the writer you believe to be, then you would have had this book written a decade ago when the notion originally popped into that little brain of yours. And do not dare tell me that it's all justified simply because you're choosing to recognize it within the confines of these pages. This book is very aware of itself, and I do not believe that merits justification."

"And therein lies my peace with it all. You bring up all of these issues, these people, these situations, and *you* tell *me* people rarely see what's in front of their face? I sleep well at night knowing this book was told from the perspective of Miles the author. The caricature. This is where the beauty of writing manifests itself so completely, because authors write to express ideas and explore areas they would not otherwise do in 'real' life. Stephen King does not purposely go out in public on a daily basis and try to frighten people. He achieves it through writing. You understand? Perceptions and judgments people make are completely theirs, and I appreciate that. Audiences should feel free to take away from this book what they choose, and what they believe, if anything at all. This is simply the story of a guy named Miles. It is not my place to tell people what I think they should take away from this or what they should or should not believe. What something means to someone may mean something entirely different to someone else. And it's my obligation to respect and listen to what others have to say. Because once someone else reads these pages, these words, the work is no longer mine. It's theirs. It's out of my hands. Yes, I finally came around and chose to listen to what you have to say, even though I may not particularly agree, I do value it. But the fact I get the biggest thrill out of people even reading my work at all, is where I find the entitlement to call myself a writer."

"Huh. I see. How moving and selfless, Miles. If you truly believe what you just said, then you should not have bitched and moaned about my presence or role in this book. I mean, we're both fully aware of the fact that I'm simply filler material. "

"Well, perhaps. But I feel it's necessary to keep you in. Maybe you do bring some sort of balance to this book that I have a hard time getting past, but somehow can't do without. I'm quite aware that people may not take kindly to a book where the author just rips on himself. But hey, self-deprecation is an easy escape."

"Interesting. However be that as it may, Miles, I'll leave you with the following. This is your first attempt at a novel, and if by some divine miracle it is even moderately successful, chances are it will be your one and only. There are a plethora of writers out there who actually have talent and legitimate writing skills, whose writing does not come off nearly as trite as yours does, and their work never sees the light of day, they never get recognized. It's a shame really, and I doubt you'll be an exception. Truth be told, there really is no way to market this book. And that will kill your chances, because sadly it really is all about money, and what will sell the most copies. And I truly hope you do not expect to see vast amounts of monies flowing your way. There are so many more books out there than there are wealthy and successful authors. If writing pieces of literary debris consistently made people rich, then everyone would be out purchasing legal pads and Bic pens. I hope you are not looking at this as a means to an end. There are over six billion people in this world, Miles, what makes you think you're so special? I will say I mildly respect the effort you made here. It was a valiant endeavor, a modest attempt, but you ultimately just take on way too much in too few pages, and you will inevitably not succeed as a writer. Do you honestly think this will be the next great American novel? It'll be the next great American joke. This is something you will need to come to terms with before those literary agent and publishing house rejection letters start rolling in. So you go on and write your final couple chapters. But try to give the readers who have made it this far a satisfactory ending, because Lord knows how much of their time you've wasted, and they're probably fairly depressed by now anyway. Sometimes the truth hurts, but it is what it is. And in the end, when everything is written and done with, and your dream of becoming a successful author is a distant, faded memory, and this book ends up in the 'we can't even sell these for a buck' bin at your local dollar store, perhaps you will find your calling, and what it is you are truly looking for.

I'll see you next time."

The Seventeenth Chapter

Magnum

A few short minutes after crossing into the northwest corner of Arkansas on Interstate 540, or Highway 71 as it was once known, I could see the Embassy Suites hotel standing proudly in the distance. The rooftop glass pyramid pointing toward the clouds.

I was back.

A mild grin came across my face as I gazed at the building, remembering my stay there only two years prior, and how my current visit was for a completely different reason, a whole other purpose. My mind quickly began to race as a nervous energy rattled my gut. I was overwhelmed by a million and one thoughts on how this could go wrong. And only one thought on how it could go right. This was the building where it could all go down. I'll either sleep alone tonight, or I won't.

It was that simple.

It was approaching 12:30 on a Saturday afternoon, in February of 2006.

I drove up to the lobby doors minutes later with a nervousness and anticipation I had never felt before. I walked into the Northwest Arkansas Embassy Suites and stood in the lobby as I looked around at the familiar setting. Not much had changed. I looked up through the open atrium to the glass rooftop pyramid I had seen from the road not ten minutes prior. I did my best to keep an optimistic, yet reserved outlook of what could happen there that night. I checked in early and was given a high floor room, as requested.

I parked my car after checking in and grabbed my bags. I rode the glass elevator up to the lucky seventh floor and unlocked the room door with ease. I walked into my room and set my bag on the bed, as was routine, yet instead of asking myself, "Okay, what now?" as I had done numerous times before, I asked myself, "Okay, where shall I put the condoms?"

The night before I was to depart on this journey I had gone to Wal-Mart to purchase a few items I hoped would play a significant role the following evening. One of them being prophylactics. I had purchased protection on previous occasions, but that was only to replace the unopened expired box that sat in my dresser drawer from the purchase before that. It was a vicious cycle of unused latex.

So have you purchased protection recently? What a confusing mess. Especially at Wal-Mart where it's constantly busy and people are always around. How can one be forced to make such a high pressure decision while surrounded by the common shopper? I mean, you've got ultra-ribbed, ultra-pleasure, ultra-thin, everything ultra. There's mint tingle, for those who enjoy the sensation of freshly brushed teeth thrown into the mix. Warm sensations, lubricated, non-lubricated, extended pleasure, Magnum. Now there's one for you. *Magnum: For the guy who has a lot more to offer.* Well I don't have a lot more to offer. I have less. So after fifteen minutes of deliberation and almost breaking into tears over the pressure, I settled on the extended pleasure, because I was going to need all of the extension available. However, they were only being sold in packages of twelve. Who needs that sort of abundance? That threw me for a loop, so I grabbed a three-pack of Durex ultra-thin and headed for the self check-out. I was not going to stand for another cashier cracking a "yeah, right"-type grin as I laid a box of condoms on the counter. *Ultra-Thin: Super thin for more feeling.* That was all well and good for me, but she's not going to be feeling anything. It would really serve in the better interest of the woman to stay home alone with the thimble game piece from Monopoly. I eventually placed the box of Durex's in the top drawer of the nightstand, right next to the Bible the Gideons had so graciously placed. A sight I found rather contrasted.

Raven was to meet me in the lobby at two o'clock. That gave me about an hour to unpack, shower, get dressed, throw some gel in my garbage hair, and hopefully have time to mix myself a drink to calm my nerves. Vodka and o.j. had also been on my Wal-Mart list. I showered up and threw on jeans with a nice blue button up. I wanted to look casual, yet confident. I failed on the second part.

I decided against mixing a drink for fear of spilling down the front of myself, and instead went down to the lobby to wait for Raven in case she arrived early. Even if she didn't arrive early I was hoping for at least on-time. A true aggravation of mine is tardiness. I find it extremely rude and off-setting. Call me a lot of things, but late is never one of them.

I sat in one of the lobby chairs to wait, and that's exactly what I did. Wait. I was constantly repositioning myself in that chair. I was very uneasy. I noticed the front desk staff would occasionally glance over at me. They probably assumed I had a problem, the way I kept squirming. Well Raven definitely did not arrive early. The two o'clock hour struck and my heart threatened to leap from my chest. I could feel tiny beads of sweat gathering on my forehead. I needed to relax. I needed a Caucasian.

2:10—Still a no show. I became a nervous train wreck. The questions and paranoia started to funnel in. What if she doesn't show? What if she's actually inside the building and can see me, but I can't see her? That must be it! I bet her and the longtime boyfriend she failed to mention are staring at me from a dark corner, laughing hysterically about what a desperate fool I was for traveling such an obscene distance under the impression that I am going to have sex with a woman completely out of my league.

2:20. Oh God! Raven and her boyfriend are going to kill me. They have probably seen what room I'm in. I'm as good as Arkansas soil. I've gotta get the hell out of here! What the hell was I thinking??

But then, before I could plan an escape, I looked up to see the lobby doors slide open, and in walked a red-headed angel that was nothing short than a gift from God. I'm not an overly religious person by any means, but at that point in my life, I think even the big guy upstairs was thinking, "Man, this fool needs a woman!" So He sent me Raven.

I stood up from my chair so Raven would notice me. She looked at me and our eyes met. Smiles fell across our faces as we walked toward each other. We came close, then stopped. Moments passed.

"Hello, Mr. Miles."

"Hello, Ms. Raven."

We both smiled again as we leaned in and put our arms around each other. She tightly held on to me. I had made it there. And so had she. She took my hand and led me out of the lobby.

"Come on."

Neither of us said anything as she led me to her car where she proceeded to pull from the back seat what I assumed could only be an overnight bag. Reality then set in. "Are you ready?" she asked. I just stared at that bag. She actually intended on staying and was asking me if I was ready. *This is really going to happen. Oh shit!* I started to internally flip-out again. What was I doing there? Of course I'm not ready! Ready for what even? My last few remaining hours here on earth? She's gonna slaughter me! Her overnight bag was probably anything but. It was more likely a kit of some sort. Lord knows what kind of tools and gadgets she had in there. Old hedge trimmers and protractors. Or perhaps she's just a complete savage in the bedroom and is into all sorts of unimaginable doings, and that bag held her supplies. My first time getting laid and I'm going to be too terrified to perform, nor do I have near the endowment or stamina to keep up with a woman of an animalistic nature. This cannot be the way I'm introduced to fornication!

"Miles ... Miles ... MILES?" Who knows how many times she had said my name before I finally snapped out of my state of terror and suspicion. "Miles, are you ready?"

"What? I'm sorry Raven. Ready for what?"

"To get something to eat," she replied, "I'm starving and I know of this great place in Fayetteville." Seeing as it was 2:30, the cocktail reception was to begin in three hours. I had never missed one, and especially did not want to that night. Raven continued as we walked back into the hotel. "Yeah, while we're over there maybe I can show you around U of A's campus too."

I bit my tongue and told her that sounded great. Despite the fact I did not want to miss any of the Embassy's cocktails, I had to remember how lucky I was she even showed up and to have her in my company in the first place. I was happy with whatever she wanted to do. We went up to the room so she could drop off her things. I was praying she would not put anything in the nightstand drawer. I think if she would have seen that box of Durex's lying there from the get go, one of only two things could have happened. Either she would have been turned on by it and we had sex immediately, or she would have verbally assaulted me and stormed out, only to never see her again. Yes, I was guessing the latter scenario as well.

We both kept bumping into each other as we were mingling around the room getting settled. An awkward laugh and an "I'm sorry" followed every bump into, so I eventually just sat on the couch and watched television while she was in the bathroom freshening up. I had gotten through the initial nervousness and anticipation of Raven actually showing up and seeing each other for the first time in two years. I was able to relax a bit. I had a gorgeous girl who was going to stay in my room with me that night. Albeit a potentially unstable amateur porn artist, but nevertheless, I felt lucky.

"You ready, Miles?" Raven asked.

"Absolutely," I said as I stood up from the couch and Raven came out of the bathroom. "You really look amazing, Raven. I mean, I just ... I'm glad you're here." I genuinely was, too.

"Me too, Miles. It's really something you coming down here. You've been a good friend and a good listener to me over the past couple of months. I never felt like you judged me for some of the crazy shit I've gone through. It's really nice to be able to talk face to face again."

I never wanted to come off as judgmental and I was glad she recognized that. I am sure she was judging herself harshly enough, and perhaps that's why she always felt the need to pour her heart out to me. Plus I would be a hypocrite to judge her when I was all too familiar with how it felt to be judged every time someone found out I had never had sex. It can be a callous world to live in when people are constantly making judgments, intentional or otherwise, without fully understanding the reasoning or background of other people. But that's the world we live in, and the world we know. We just have to keep moving on.

Raven shot me a wink and a smile as we left the room. We hopped in her car and took off. Fayetteville was not as far of a drive as I had anticipated. As usual, Raven did most of the talking in the car and I interjected when I wanted. But I didn't mind. My financial and educational woes were not burdening my every thought for a change. It was a sunny February afternoon and I was soaking up the scenery and conversation, and for the first time in a long while, I found myself feeling truly happy.

Raven drove me around Fayetteville and the campus at the University of Arkansas. I always found it enjoyable going to other colleges and noticing the similarities and differences from that of my own. She was thrilled and eager about graduation that following May and even showed me a copy of the resume she was working on. She told me she wanted to take advantage of my proofreading abilities (which have been pointed out to be a bit lacking), so I took a moment and looked it over for her and made a few suggestions. I did not, however, overlook the fact that her brief stint in the adult film industry was absent from the "work experience" section, but I kept those comments to myself.

We eventually made it to the restaurant when I glanced at my watch, and it appeared we were going to miss part of the Embassy's cocktail hour. This is going to sound wretched and shallow, but I had heard over the years from guys who were actually successful with women that they lasted much longer in bed as a result of having a significant amount of alcohol in their system. I had no way of ever testing that theory so I just went with it, which was why I was so concerned about getting back for the cocktails. I obviously did not want to get hammered and end up ruining things, but if a passion-filled evening was on the horizon and that theory proved to be true, then I wanted to start drinking as soon as possible. In moderation, of course.

After we were seated, I was hoping our server would first ask Raven what she would like to drink. If she ordered alcohol it would not have made me feel as guilty about doing the same, seeing it was only a little past 4:30 and I did not want to start drinking if she wasn't going to.

"What'll it be, miss?" our server asked.

"I'll have a strawberry daiquiri."

What a relief. I ordered a Blue Moon and that was that, another unnecessary worry behind me. There the two of us were, chatting and laughing over drinks just as we had twenty-three months prior. Only now we knew much more about each other. The evening was going perfectly. She had me try fried alligator for the first time, and I convinced her that mayonnaise and ketchup mixed together *did* taste great on fries. We just clicked, Raven and I, and I took every moment in stride.

After we ate and had a few more drinks, we eventually agreed that getting back to the hotel would be best. I was relieved she wanted to return to the Embassy because we could easily have drank ourselves to the point of a taxi ride back to her place which was much closer, a scenario which I'm sure would have worked out, but one I wanted to avoid with good reason. Remember after all, my ultimate demise may have been her goal that evening. Didn't any of you see the film *Monster*?

It was approaching 7:00 p.m. as we returned to the Embassy. An hour and a half of discounted booze missed! But I didn't mind at that point. We moseyed our way over to the same lobby couch we sat in the first time we met and I fetched us two screwdrivers. Raven sat with her legs crossed wearing jeans and a top that seemed to be custom made for her. They completely showed off her amazing figure. Her auburn-red hair seemed longer than I remembered and flowed past her shoulders and down her back. I really had no clue why she was with me. Was she *that* grateful someone listened to her problems and such? Perhaps it was just that. I actually listened and talked with her instead of trying to hit on her and be all macho and inappropriate. But then again maybe that strength weakened me. Not pursuing women more aggressively and not being strongly confident in myself or whatever. Was I a walking cliché that nice guys really do come in last? Possibly. But at least I never tried being someone different.

Raven and I finished our one and only Embassy provided cocktail. It seemed the hours were passing too quickly. I had just arrived for God's sake! She and I high-tailed it to the hotel bar where I opened a tab that would ultimately be picked up by the folks over at American Express. As we periodically remarked on some of the other guests, I excused myself to the restroom because I had been ferociously holding it since the restaurant. I stood at the urinal and took a deep breath. I suddenly remembered that man from the same urinal who told me life only stands still when you're taking a piss. He creeped me out at the time, but I realized then that he was right. I was able to stand there and gather my thoughts. It was getting later in the night as Raven and I harbored a healthy buzz.

It was approaching half past nine when Raven asked out of the blue, "Miles, why did you come here?" Her middle finger slowly worked its way around the rim of her glass. "Was it to get a story for your book?"

I was more shocked than offended she asked such a question.

"My book?" I asked.

Raven took a drink. "Yes, the book you want to write."

"Raven, I told you that I only *tell* people I'm writing a book. I'll probably never do so, I'm too lazy. I just want the damn thing to write itself. The book has nothing to do with me being here."

"Well ... I just thought maybe I could be in your book, you know? Wouldn't you like that?"

I feared she may start to break down on me.

"Raven, you are so pretty, and so sweet, but I think of you as so much more than just a character in some book that will probably never exist. Don't you know that? I would not be here if you didn't completely blow me away. Every time we speak, every time I looked at your pictures, I was awed. I felt blessed. That's why I'm here, Raven. I'm here for you, and only you. Not for motivation for some stupid book. Plus, I don't even know how I would use you in a story."

Raven leaned in close to me. "I've got an idea."

She put her hand on my cheek while she leaned in a little further and began to kiss me. I wasn't sure what to think.

"Ehem," the bartender interrupted, "not at the bar please."

Raven stopped and sat back, polishing off her drink. I stared at her as I spoke to the bartender. "We're sorry, but I'll take the bill now." The bartender gave me my tab and I scribbled on the dotted line, never losing eye contact with Raven.

The time was now. She gave me the go ahead. It seemed as if the moment I waited almost twenty-three years for was upon me. Her and I left the bar, hand in hand, and jetted for the elevators. Our hands were all over each other in the glass elevators and anyone who looked up could witness the inappropriateness of it all. If I thought the anticipation before was overwhelming, I could barely contain myself as we approached the room. She had the room key and fumbled to get the door unlocked. I had my hands on her hips as I looked behind me and down through the atrium. I took another deep breath. This was going to be it. How drunk was I? More importantly, how drunk was she? Didn't matter. I then heard a click.

"Got it!" she yelled. Raven opened the door as I put my hands around her waist. She turned around and we embraced each other tightly as we headed straight for the couch, the door slammed shut behind us.

The intensity of what was happening gained momentum quickly. If something was going to happen, I did not want it to be on that couch. I also did not want everything to start happening immediately either. I know – such demands. Probably another reason it took almost a quarter century for this to occur. It was becoming rather primal on that couch and I wanted to slow things down a bit.

Raven lifted her shirt over her head and I began unbuttoning mine. So much for slowing. I was sitting up on the couch and she was on top of me. The sounds of locked lips and heavy breathing filled the room. She reached behind her back and unhooked her bra as I undid my last button. I removed my shirt and hurled it to the floor, her bra quickly followed. I could feel her spine as I pressed her body against mine. Flesh against flesh. We continued to kiss heavily as our hands explored each other. Her hair brushed my chest.

Several minutes had passed before I picked her up while she wrapped her legs around me. I carried Raven into the bedroom and laid her on the bed. I stood there as she started unbuckling her belt and removing her jeans. I quickly followed. It was getting close and did not matter how much alcohol I had in my system. I knew right then it was going to be brief.

We exchanged mischievous grins as I pushed my boxers down to my ankles and she lifted her body, removing her panties. I climbed on the bed. The heat between our skin grew as the unattained passion intensified. Our legs intertwined as our bodies caressed. Her flawless body against my very much imperfect one. Nothing still made any sense to me, but at that moment I could have cared less.

Now allow me to do us all a favor and spare the more intimate details as I do not want this to turn into one of those trashy romance novels more so than it already has. That's not to say the book isn't at all trashy, but I have a hard enough time with myself in these types of situations, let alone what you poor readers must be imagining!

Time passed and it came to the point where I was in a prime position to reach into the nightstand and grab an ultra-thin. We momentarily stopped what we were doing and looked at each other. Raven smiled and pushed her hair back.

"Hang on a sec, baby," Raven said. She rolled over onto her stomach at the edge of the bed and reached into her overnight bag. The notion briefly entered my brain that she was searching for the proper tool to bludgeon me with. I started to reach for the nightstand, but was ultimately too late. Raven leaned up and stuck out her hand.

"Here, use this." I took what she had and looked down.

MAGNUM.

WHAT?! Is she out of her mind?? Everything was out there. We were completely exposed. It was blatantly obvious both of us knew I could not sustain so much latex. The thing should have been blown up and made to be a float in the Macy's Thanksgiving Day Parade to promote safe sex. But what was I going to do? Ruin the mood and reach into the nightstand and politely ask, "Um, excuse me sweetheart. I don't want to be rude, but would you mind if we used these significantly smaller prophylactics?" Well I really didn't have a choice. I slipped on that latex Hindenburg with more excess to spare than I care to admit.

I took Raven in my arms and laid back on the bed with her. I positioned myself on top and gave her a slow, meaningful kiss. I placed my hand on her cheek as her body arched up, and she allowed me in to her little secret garden.

This was it. The ultimate human connection. The absolute basis of life. I was physically inside of another human being. The warm sensation of it all. The heat. The passion. The loss of innocence. Was this what it was *all* about? Had I finally found what I was looking for?

It is often said that virgins are easy to detect. Sometimes it's the way they act when sex is brought up. Occasionally it's the way they talk about sex. But more often than not, they are exposed by the person who takes that innocence, if it was not already admitted to. How do most women know if they're having sex with a virgin? Because the act is over in about as much time as it takes to toast bread.

I was no exception.

That Magnum served its purpose shortly after I applied it. All that build up, all that anticipation, always hearing people say how amazing it is, how magical. And for what? "Oh..., oh God!" And **boom**, toast is done. Indeed it is special, but the longevity is almost non-existent, and I can almost guarantee Raven knew what had just happened, knew what I had just lost, but she never said a word.

I could not bring myself to even look at her. How ashamed I was. How embarrassed really. The way I saw it was that I had about six seconds to decide whether I would attempt to maintain this thing or have it end on a very premature note.

I reached over into the nightstand and grabbed a more appropriately fitting Durex. I replaced the Magnum as Raven and I embraced each other once more. I faired a little better the second time around. Same as I had with my ACT's. I tried to take my time and be more conscious of what I was actually doing, because it was that time around I knew what drew me to see her again in the first place. It was not strictly the appeal of sex, even though that was the underlying force. It was because I felt this void in my life. A missing piece. A certain emptiness in my heart. I had finally discovered with Raven the deepest of connections, and was experiencing a little piece of heaven, right here on earth.

The Complexities of Intimacy

I had a difficult time sleeping that night, as we both lay naked under the sheets. I stared up at the ceiling wondering if Raven would ever fully realize the significant role she played in my little life. There was a part of me which thought she had to of known I had never been with a woman before, particularly if she did in fact star in that video. If indeed she had, being with me would have been like staying in a Ritz-Carlton one night and the next night staying in a ... oh ... I can't even say the words ... Motel 6. Good God! Motel 6—where they'll keep the light on for ya'. Yeah, well, here's to hoping it's a black light.

Lying there, I mulled over, oddly enough, the huge significance that beds have in our lives. Major events in life happen while we're in bed. Good and bad. Babies are conceived in bed. Relationships sometimes fail because of inadequacies between the sheets. We spend a third of our lives sleeping in them. People die in bed. Innocence is lost. Married couples talk about how they have fallen out of love, and how they're going to tell their children. Sometimes we make believe we're invisible, and that we can disappear from life's problems if we simply hide under our covers. Beds are something we look forward to every night, if fortunate enough to have one. It's amazing what happens in the same place we dream.

The few hours of sleep I did get consisted of falling in and out of the same dream. I was a small child running in what seemed to be an empty, remote golden field where there was nothing around in all directions. I was running and chasing after a white figure that was off in the distance. Then I'd wake up. I'd quickly fall back asleep and the dream would again begin, each time the figure appeared further and further away. I was running as fast as my little legs would allow, but the figure kept getting smaller and smaller, and by the final time I drifted back into the dream, the figure had disappeared. I stopped running and was breathing very heavily. I just stood in that open field and started to cry, never knowing who or what I was chasing, or why. All of a sudden the phone rang and I awoke from the dream, my eyes watery.

It was already nine o'clock the next morning and I had requested a wake-up call because I wanted to make sure we did not miss the breakfast like we had the cocktail hour. I rolled over on my side to discover Raven asleep on her back, her breasts exposed as the sheets had worked their way down her body during the night. I slid the sheets up to cover her.

"Raven?" I whispered, "wake up sweetheart. Raven?"

"Huh? What?" She slowly began waking up. "What are you doing?"

"You were uncovered so I pulled the sheets up over you."

"Oh. Well what time is it?"

"Nine."

"Ugh. I don't want to wake up! God, my head!" She pulled the sheet up over her face. "Would you scoot over?"

She seemed adamant about me not being next to her, so I inched myself back to my side of the bed.

"Breakfast is going to be over soon," I said, "you should probably take a shower if you want."

"I would rather just lay here. You can go."

"Well it would be nice if you came. I have to be on the road in a few hours and I'd like to spend a little more time together."

"Fine!! Whatever!" Raven was a bit short with me and was not acting like the girl from the night before, or who had confessed basically her entire life to me up until that point. I rode it off as perhaps she was just not a morning person.

Raven climbed out of bed and headed into the bathroom. The entire room was dark except for the bit of light from behind the curtains and the bathroom light which was shining against the adjacent wall. Raven left the bathroom door open as she stood in front of the mirror. I laid in bed and gazed at the light against the wall. In the middle of that light danced the outline of Raven's body. Her stunning silhouette. I watched peacefully, and I could not fathom the thought of how in the hell I was so blessed as to be allowed a girl like that, any girl really. A person of such grace. As the shadow of her body appeared before me, I finally understood that there is no greater gift than that of a woman. None of us would be here without them, nor do men go to greater lengths than to be with them. The female body is, above all else, the most natural beauty found amongst all things.

I took a shower as Raven brushed and blow dried her hair. She finished before me, and I walked out of the bathroom to notice her overnight bag was packed up on the bed.

"You ready to go?" Raven asked. I turned around and found her standing at the door.

"Um ... alright." She and I headed down the elevator and to the breakfast area in almost complete silence. Something was definitely different. I feared she may have realized my secret, and was upset that I did not tell her about it. After getting our trays, plates, and silverware, Raven immediately branched off to the fresh fruit buffet while I waited in line for a ham and cheese omelet. I tipped the short order chef before making my way around to all the buffets. It took me a minute to spot where Raven had sat. Once I did, I took a deep breath and headed over.

"This all looks great," I said as I sat down across from her in an effort to break up the awkward silence that had found its way between us. Raven simply raised her eyebrows a bit as she stared down at her plate. I could not understand what her sudden change in attitude was all about, or what warranted it. She had told me everything under the sun about herself, but could not tell me the issue at hand?

We sat silent as we ate our breakfast. She mostly picked at her fruit. I was half way through my omelet as I picked up a piece of bacon and took a bite. That's when I heard my name.

"Miles?"

I rolled my eyes up to find Raven staring at me. I did not even have time to respond before she said those seven words.

"I don't think we should talk anymore."

I sat there, blank faced, motionless, and felt nothing after what she said. Perhaps I should have seen this coming. I set down my bacon, placed my elbows on the table, and crossed my hands in front of my face. As Raven continued staring at me expecting some kind of response, I turned my head to the right and took notice of all the surrounding guests.

God there is a lot of people in this world.

That is when I noticed a young boy chasing a young girl in a white dress.

He chased after her as they smiled and giggled, the girl never once turned around to see how close the boy was. It reminded me of my dream. The simple innocence of childhood surrounded them, and they seemed not to care which way they were headed. It calmed me.

I turned my head and faced Raven with peaceful eyes. I said one word in a soft voice, hoping she would realize that I was not upset, because for some strange reason, I wasn't.

"Okay."

We stared at each other for a moment, but I don't think either of us were actually looking. She took a sip of her orange juice and I took one last bite of bacon. Breakfast was over.

On the elevator ride up, which could not have less resembled the ride we took twelve hours prior, she informed me she planned on leaving as soon as she got her things, as if I had not already suspected such. I unlocked the door and let her in. I waited for her by the atrium balcony outside the room as I watched and listened to silverware banging away at plates as people finished their breakfast. I heard the door open behind me shortly thereafter and turned around to see Raven with her bag hanging off of her right shoulder. We took the elevator down to the lobby. Why I felt the need to walk her out baffled me. I guess I was hoping for some sort of closure.

I had my head down as I was walking a few feet behind Raven and could hear the sound of her footsteps in front of me, until they abruptly stopped. Raven turned around in front of the lobby doors and we once again found ourselves staring at each other, only this time I could tell we were actually seeing each other for what one another truly was. My face was blank, but I mustered up half a grin as I took a step closer. She adjusted the bag on her shoulder. I slowly leaned in, took her hand, and gently kissed her cheek. I whispered in her ear.

"Thank you."

I let go of her hand and stepped back. She looked down at the ground for a moment and then back up at me.

"Maybe this can be your ending."

She gave me a little smile and turned around to head for the doors. I watched that auburn hair bounce off her shoulders as she walked away, never once turning around to see if I was chasing after her. I stood still and watched her walk out of the doors and out of my life. I knew I would never see her again. And it would not be until years later when I would realize what her last words to me meant, and how right she was.

I turned my back to the doors and headed toward the elevator, taking notice of the hotel bar where we had sat and shared innocent conversation two years prior, and again the night before. I immediately started to pack my bag up in the room and tried to sort out what had just quickly unfolded that morning. I truly had no intention of starting a relationship with Raven, and I am sure she felt the same of me. But to have so many meaningful conversations over those few months, and to invite me down two years after our first encounter solely on the basis of sex, and then never again wanting to speak to me? I kept pondering it over and over. Perhaps she did this kind of thing all the time. One woman's insatiable need to see how far she can get men to come to be with her, and I was just another step along her way. I thought about what Valerie had said as I wondered if sex truly does define us. The lengths we go to achieve it, and the hearts we break after it. I was in no position to answer that question, but perhaps Raven was, and that was the difference between her and I, the difference she recognized, but knew I did not. And maybe she left so I could go on and figure it out for myself, but I am not sure I will ever know. It's just one of those things I need to let be.

I checked out of the Embassy Suites shortly thereafter, filling my car up with gas before I left the great state of Arkansas, leaving a changed man, but basically feeling numb. I had driven a good while into Missouri when I realized my Dave Matthews Band had not been playing in the car. That's a rare thing. However, I found the silence comforting that afternoon, so I decided to leave it that way.

As I continued northeast through the vastness of the Missouri Valley, I was not really thinking about anything in particular. I was merely driving in silence along a stretch of highway where no other cars were visible. I was alone. And to my surprise, a smile started to find its way across my face. As the smile grew larger, tears began to well up in my eyes. And as the tears formed, I began to laugh. Tears started to fall as laughter echoed through the car, and the harder I laughed, the quicker tears streamed down my face. It was the most surreal moment of my life. Laughing and crying at the same time, without really knowing why. Perhaps it was just simply that my heart was breaking. It was a powerful mix of emotions which I do not think any other circumstance could have provoked. I realized no matter how beautiful

Raven was on the outside, what she had inside was not a true reflection. I finally realized then that true beauty is found within those who have the ability to first look at what's inside, and perhaps that was something I did not possess. But as I drove on alone, I knew an emptiness in my life had been filled, and that what I was experiencing right then was not about the journey I had taken, it was not about Raven or the connection we had, it was not even about the intimacy we shared.

It was about something more.

I found some peace looking out over the empty Missouri landscape as tears and laughter poured from my face. And I could not help but to take in, and be thankful for, the beautiful, calming nothingness that can sometimes be found in this one, sweet world.

giving2green

The giving2green symbol indicates that the user has committed to giving monies to the many organizations dedicated to the fight against global warming, decreasing greenhouse gas emissions, saving our rainforests and wetlands, and fighting water and air pollution.

giving2green gives 100 percent of its proceeds to supporting the organizations fighting these battles. Because we feel that saving our planet and the people, plants, and animals inhabiting it is one of the most critical challenges we face today, we request that all our authors commit their support as well.

We feel good about making a difference. Every little bit helps, and today's businesses should step up to the challenge of not only doing their part, but setting an example—not just because it's good for our environment, but because it's the right thing to do.

20215582R00065

Made in the USA
Lexington, KY
25 January 2013